ELECTRICAL MOTOR CONTROLS

for *Integrated Systems*

Third Edition

Workbook

AMERICAN TECHNICAL PUBLISHERS, INC.
HOMEWOOD, ILLINOIS 60430-4600

Gary J. Rockis
Glen A. Mazur

Electrical Motor Controls for Integrated Systems Workbook contains procedures commonly practiced in industry and the trade. Specific procedures vary with each task and must be performed by a qualified person. For maximum safety, always refer to specific manufacturer recommendations, insurance regulations, specific job site and plant procedures, applicable federal, state, and local regulations, and any authority having jurisdiction. The material contained is intended to be an educational resource for the user. American Technical Publishers, Inc., assumes no responsibility or liability in connection with this material or its use by any individual or organization.

© 2005 by American Technical Publishers, Inc.
All rights reserved

3 4 5 6 7 8 9 – 05 – 9 8 7 6 5 4 3 2

Printed in the United States of America

ISBN 0-8269-1208-7

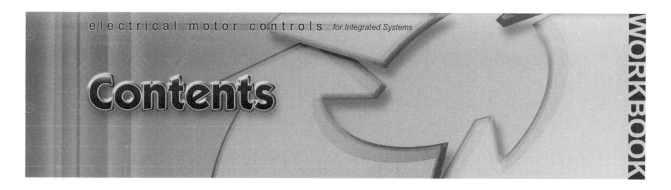

electrical motor controls *for Integrated Systems*

WORKBOOK

Contents

5 LOGIC APPLIED TO LINE DIAGRAMS

6 SOLENOIDS, DC GENERATORS, AND DC MOTORS

7 AC GENERATORS, TRANSFORMERS, AND AC MOTORS

8 CONTACTORS AND MOTOR STARTERS

9 CONTROL DEVICES

9 CONTROL DEVICES (continued)

10 REVERSING MOTOR CIRCUITS

11 POWER DISTRIBUTION SYSTEMS

12 SOLID-STATE DEVICES AND SYSTEM INTEGRATION

13   TIMERS AND COUNTERS

14   RELAYS AND SOLID-STATE STARTERS

15   SENSING DEVICES AND CONTROLS

16   PROGRAMMABLE CONTROLLERS

16 **PROGRAMMABLE CONTROLLERS** (continued)

17 **REDUCED-VOLTAGE STARTING**

18 **ACCELERATING AND DECELERATING METHODS**

19 **PREVENTIVE MAINTENANCE AND TROUBLESHOOTING**

A **APPENDIX**   **249**

electrical motor controls *for Integrated Systems*

Introduction

WORKBOOK

Electrical Motor Controls for Integrated Systems Workbook is designed to reinforce the concepts and provide system design activities for the material presented in *Electrical Motor Controls for Integrated Systems,* 3rd Edition. When studying the textbook, pay particular attention to italicized terms, illustrations, and examples. These key elements comprise a major portion of the workbook.

Tech-Cheks

The workbook contains 19 Tech-Cheks. Each Tech-Chek is a series of multiple choice, completion, and/or matching questions that are based on the text and art in the corresponding chapter of the textbook. Always study the assigned chapter of the textbook thoroughly before completing the Tech-Cheks.

Worksheets

The workbook contains 152 Worksheets developed from the 19 chapters of the textbook. Worksheets provide opportunities to apply the concepts and theory in the textbook to practical design problems. See the table of contents for a complete listing.

Appendix

The Appendix contains Data Sheets, charts, and tables for use with the Worksheets. See page 249 for a complete listing of Data Sheets, charts, and tables in the Appendix.

Related Information

Information presented in *Electrical Motor Controls for Integrated Systems,* 3rd Edition, and *Electrical Motor Controls for Integrated Systems Workbook* addresses common electrical motor control system topics. Additional information related to electrical motor control systems is available in other American Tech products. To obtain information about these products, visit the American Tech web site at www.go2atp.com.

The Authors and Publisher

Electrical Quantities and Circuits

Tech-Chek 1

Name _____ Date _____

Electrical Motor Controls

_____ 1. ___ is the most common source of energy used to produce electricity.
A. Oil   C. Nuclear power
B. Coal   D. Water

_____ 2. ___ energy is stored energy a body has due to its position.

_____ 3. ___ is the amount of electrical pressure in a circuit.
A. Power   C. Resistance
B. Current   D. Voltage

_____ 4. A(n) ___ connection is a connection that has two or more components connected so there is only one path for current flow.

_____ 5. ___ is the amount of electrons flowing through an electrical circuit.
A. Power   C. Resistance
B. Current   D. Voltage

_____ 6. A(n) ___ is an electrical device that uses electromagnetism to change voltage from one level to another.

_____ 7. A(n) ___ unit is a number that does not include a metric prefix.

_____ 8. ___ power is the product of voltage and current in a circuit calculated without considering the phase shift that may be present between the voltage and current.

_____ 9. ___ is the rate of doing work or using energy.
A. Power   C. Resistance
B. Current   D. Voltage

_____ 10. ___ power is the actual power used in an electrical circuit.

_____ 11. ___ is the opposition to the flow of electrons.
A. Power   C. Resistance
B. Current   D. Voltage

_____ 12. The current in a circuit containing ___ loads is the same throughout the circuit.

_____ 13. ___ is the property of a circuit that causes it to oppose a change in current due to energy stored in a magnetic field.
A. Capacitance C. Inductance
B. Phase shift D. Frequency

_____ 14. ___ is the ratio of true power in an AC circuit to apparent power delivered to the circuit.

_____15. Ohm's law states that voltage in a circuit is equal to ___ .
         A. current times resistance   C. resistance divided by current
         B. current divided by   D. resistance divided by power
             resistance

_____16. The power formula states that power in a circuit is equal to___.
         A. voltage divided by current   C. resistance divided by current
         B. current divided by voltage   D. voltage times current

_____17. The voltage across each load in a(n) ___ circuit is the same.

_____18. In circuits that contain inductance or capacitance, the opposition to the flow of current is ___.
         A. resistance   C. reactance
         B. apparent power   D. frequency

_____19. A(n) ___ connection is a connection that has two or more components connected so there is more than one path for current flow.

_____20. In circuits that contain resistance and reactance, the combined opposition to the flow of current is ___.

Electrical Measurements

_____ 1. The meter test leads are connected in parallel with a lamp. There is a negative sign in front of the reading and the negative sign disappears when the test leads are reversed.

      A. DC voltage measurement
      B. DC in-line current measurement
      C. Resistance measurement
      D. Clamp-on current measurement

_____ 2. The circuit is opened just before a lamp and the meter test leads are connected into the opening. There is a negative sign in front of the reading and the negative sign disappears when the test leads are reversed.

_____ 3. One conductor is enclosed in the jaws of the meter attachment and the measurement is taken.

_____ 4. The power to the circuit is turned OFF and meter test leads are connected across the component under test.

Electrical Quantities and Circuits

Worksheet 1-1

Name _____ Date _____

Prefixes

List each equivalent value in the units given.

_____ **1.** 13.8 kV = ___ V

_____ **2.** 27 mA = ___ A

_____ **3.** 200 μA = ___ mA

_____ **4.** 200 μA = ___ A

_____ **5.** 12 MW = ___ kW

_____ **6.** 3.3 A = ___ mA

_____ **7.** 4.7 MΩ = ___ Ω

_____ **8.** 1.12 mW = ___ μW

_____ **9.** .050 kVA = ___ VA

_____ **10.** 16.6 kV = ___ MV

Electrical Quantities

Match the unit of measurement with the equivalent abbreviation.

_____ **1.** Ohm

_____ **2.** Ampere

_____ **3.** Watt

_____ **4.** Farad

_____ **5.** Henry

_____ **6.** Volt

_____ **7.** Hertz

_____ **8.** Siemens

_____ **9.** Second

_____ **10.** Volt-amp

A. S
B. s
C. V
D. A
E. Ω
F. W
G. VA
H. F
I. H
J. Hz

Electrical Quantities and Circuits

Worksheet 1-2

Name _____ Date _____

Current Flow

Mark the polarity of each component (+ or −) and use arrows to indicate the direction of current flow through the components.

1. Indicate the direction of conventional current flow.

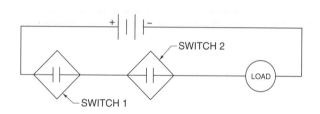

SERIES-CONNECTED SWITCHES

2. Indicate the direction of electron current flow.

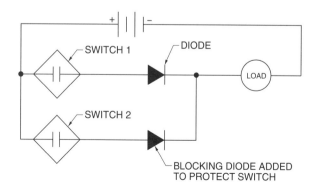

PARALLEL-CONNECTED SWITCHES

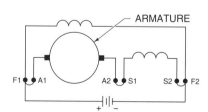

Electrical Quantities and Circuits

Worksheet 1-3

Name _____ Date _____

Multimeter Basic Measurements

Draw the correct position of the function switches to measure the electrical quantity based on the meter connections and circuit.

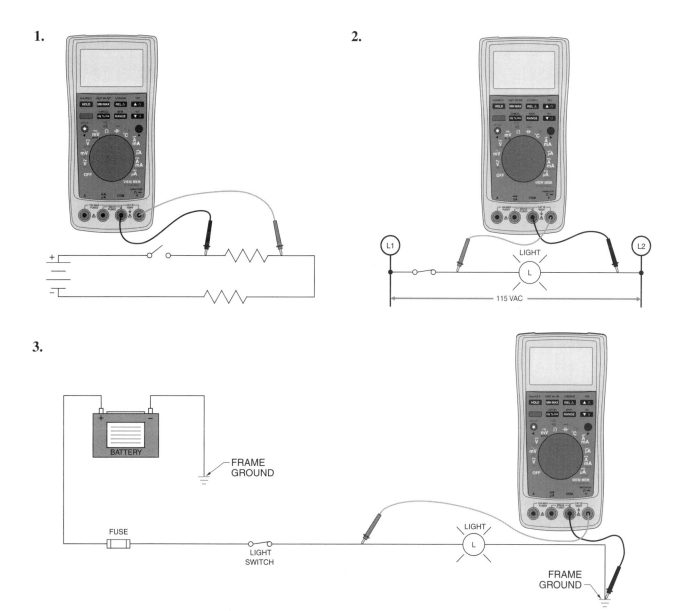

Electrical Quantities and Circuits

Worksheet 1-4

Name _____ Date _____

Ohm's Law
Solve for the unknown quantity.

_____ 1. E = ___ V

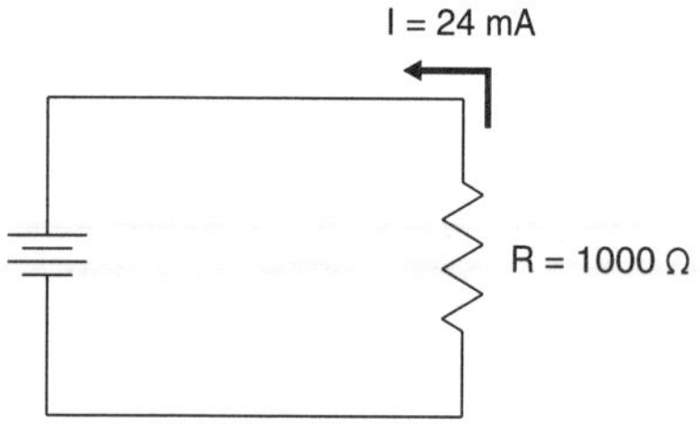

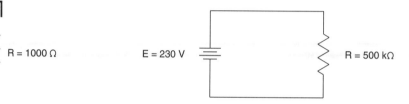

I = 24 mA
R = 1000 Ω

_____ 2. I = ___ μA

E = 230 V
R = 500 kΩ

_____ 3. R = ___ Ω

I = 12 mA
E = 12 V

_____ 4. I = ___ μA

E = 460 V
R = 1 MΩ

_____ 5. E = ___ V

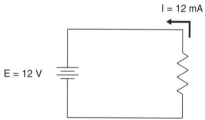

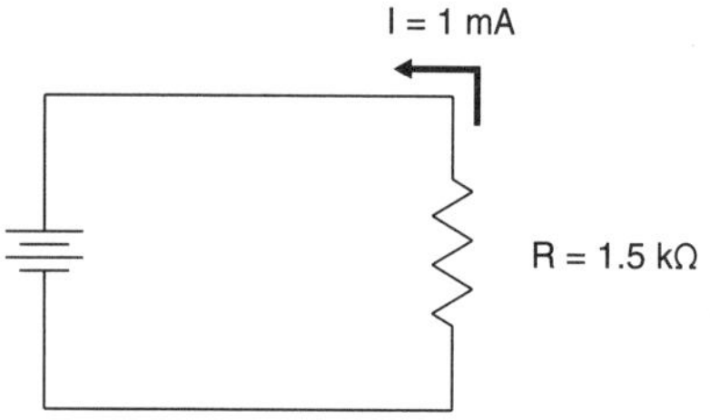

I = 1 mA
R = 1.5 kΩ

_____ 6. R = ___ kΩ

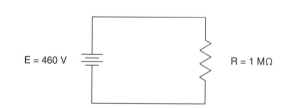

I = 4 mA
E = 6 V

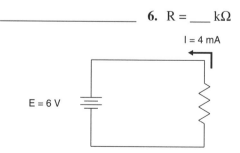

Electrical Quantities and Circuits

Worksheet 1-5

Name _____ Date _____

Power Formula

Solve for the unknown quantity.

_____ **1.** P = ___ mW

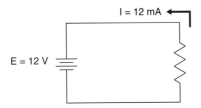

_____ **2.** I = ___ mA

_____ **3.** P = ___ mW

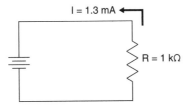

_____ **4.** I = ___ A

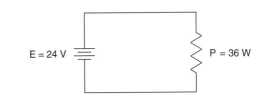

_____ **5.** P = ___ W

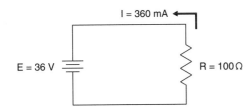

_____ **6.** R = ___ kΩ

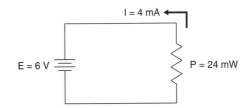

Electrical Quantities and Circuits

Worksheet 1-6

Name _____ Date _____

Series Circuit Resistance

Determine the total resistance of each circuit.

_____ **1.** $R_T =$ ___ $k\Omega$

$R_1 = 1000\ \Omega$ $R_2 = 1\ k\Omega$

$R_3 = .001\ M\Omega$

_____ **2.** $R_T =$ ___ Ω

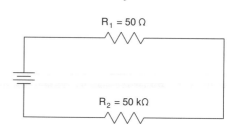

$R_1 = 50\ \Omega$

$R_2 = 50\ k\Omega$

_____ **3.** $R_T =$ ___ $M\Omega$

$R_1 = 50\ M\Omega$

$R_2 = 50\ k\Omega$

_____ **4.** $R_T =$ ___ $k\Omega$

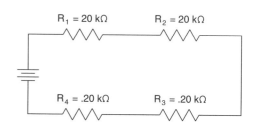

$R_1 = 20\ k\Omega$ $R_2 = 20\ k\Omega$

$R_4 = .20\ k\Omega$ $R_3 = .20\ k\Omega$

_____ **5.** $R_T =$ ___ Ω

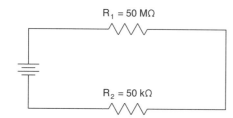

$R_1 = 1.2\ k\Omega$ $R_2 = 1.2\ k\Omega$

$R_3 = 1.2\ k\Omega$

_____ **6.** $R_T =$ ___ Ω

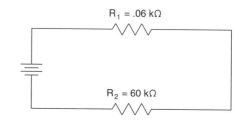

$R_1 = .06\ k\Omega$

$R_2 = 60\ k\Omega$

Electrical Quantities and Circuits

Worksheet 1-7

Name _____   Date _____

Series Circuit Voltage/Current/Power

Determine the unknown quantity.

_____ **1.** E = ___ V

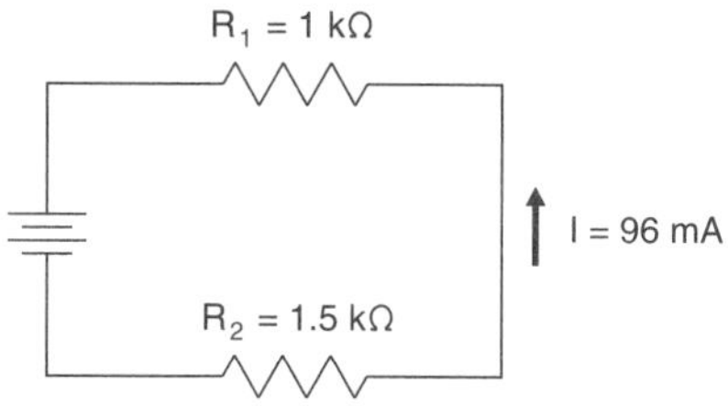

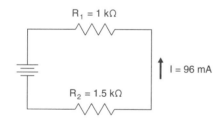

_____ **2.** I = ___ A

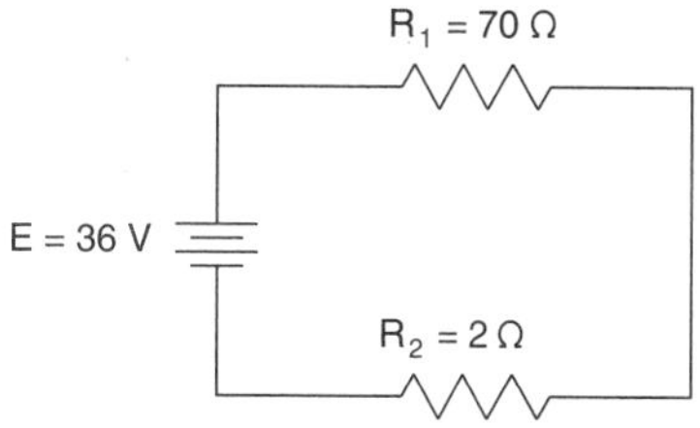

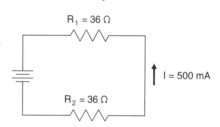

_____ **3.** P_T = ___ W

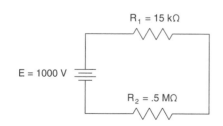

_____ **4.** P_T = ___ W

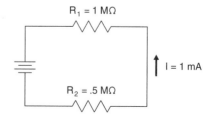

_____ **5.** I = ___ mA

_____ **6.** E = ___ kV

Electrical Quantities and Circuits

Worksheet 1-8

Name _____ Date _____

Parallel Circuit Resistance

Determine the total resistance of each circuit. Round to the nearest ohm.

_____ **1.** R_T = ___ Ω

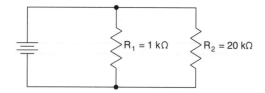

_____ **2.** R_T = ___ Ω

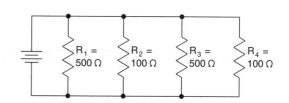

_____ **3.** R_T = ___ Ω

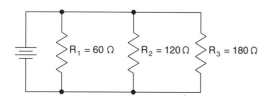

_____ **4.** R_T = ___ Ω

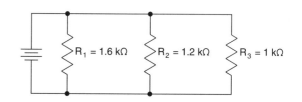

_____ **5.** R_T = ___ Ω

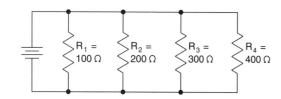

_____ **6.** R_T = ___ Ω

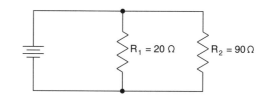

Worksheet 1-9

Name _____ Date _____

Parallel Circuit Voltage/Current/Power
Determine the unknown quantity.

_____ **1.** $P_T = $ ___ kW

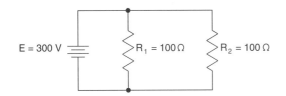

$E = 300\ V$ $R_1 = 100\ \Omega$ $R_2 = 100\ \Omega$

_____ **2.** $I_T = $ ___ A

$E = 225\ V$ $R_1 = 30\ \Omega$ $R_2 = 90\ \Omega$

_____ **3.** $P_2 = $ ___ W

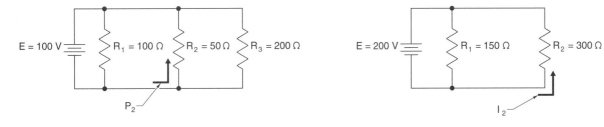

$E = 100\ V$ $R_1 = 100\ \Omega$ $R_2 = 50\ \Omega$ $R_3 = 200\ \Omega$

P_2

_____ **4.** $I_2 = $ ___ A

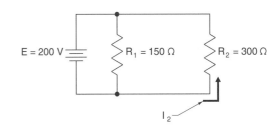

$E = 200\ V$ $R_1 = 150\ \Omega$ $R_2 = 300\ \Omega$

I_2

_____ **5.** $P_3 = $ ___ W

$E = 100\ V$ $R_1 = 100\ \Omega$ $R_2 = 50\ \Omega$ $R_3 = 200\ \Omega$

P_3

_____ **6.** $I_1 = $ ___ A

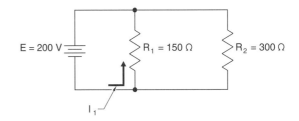

$E = 200\ V$ $R_1 = 150\ \Omega$ $R_2 = 300\ \Omega$

I_1

Electrical Quantities and Circuits

Worksheet 1-10

Name _____   Date _____

Series/Parallel Circuit Resistance

Determine the total resistance of each circuit.

_____ **1.** $R_T =$ ___ Ω

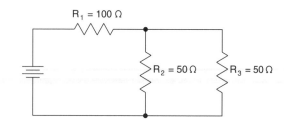

_____ **2.** $R_T =$ ___ Ω

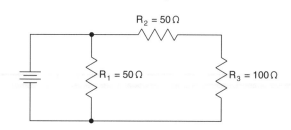

_____ **3.** $R_T =$ ___ Ω

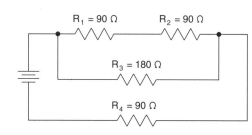

_____ **4.** $R_T =$ ___ Ω

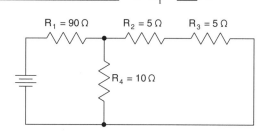

_____ **5.** $R_T =$ ___ Ω

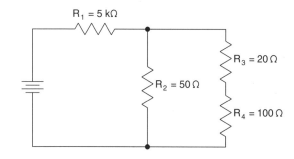

_____ **6.** $R_T =$ ___ Ω

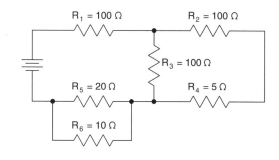

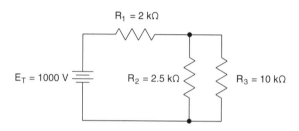

Electrical Quantities and Circuits

Worksheet 1-11

Name _____ Date _____

Series/Parallel Circuit Voltage/Current/Power

Determine the unknown quantity.

_____ **1.** $I_T =$ ___ mA

$R_1 = 2\ k\Omega$
$E_T = 1000\ V$ $R_2 = 2.5\ k\Omega$ $R_3 = 10\ k\Omega$

_____ **2.** $I_4 =$ ___ A

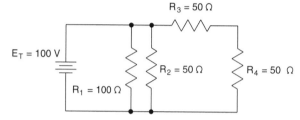

$R_3 = 50\ \Omega$
$E_T = 100\ V$ $R_2 = 50\ \Omega$ $R_4 = 50\ \Omega$
$R_1 = 100\ \Omega$

_____ **3.** $E_T =$ ___ V

$R_1 = 16\ \Omega$
$R_2 = 20\ \Omega$ $R_3 = 80\ \Omega$
$I_T = 1\ A$

_____ **4.** $I_T =$ ___ A

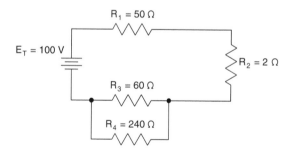

$R_1 = 50\ \Omega$
$E_T = 100\ V$ $R_2 = 2\ \Omega$
$R_3 = 60\ \Omega$
$R_4 = 240\ \Omega$

_____ **5.** $E_T =$ ___ V

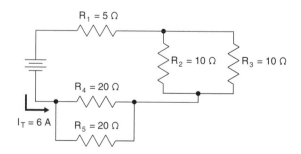

$R_1 = 5\ \Omega$
$R_2 = 10\ \Omega$ $R_3 = 10\ \Omega$
$R_4 = 20\ \Omega$
$I_T = 6\ A$ $R_5 = 20\ \Omega$

_____ **6.** $E_T =$ ___ V

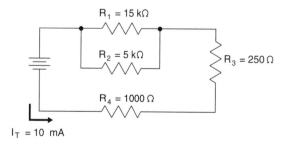

$R_1 = 15\ k\Omega$
$R_2 = 5\ k\Omega$ $R_3 = 250\ \Omega$
$R_4 = 1000\ \Omega$
$I_T = 10\ mA$

Electrical Quantities and Circuits

Name _____ Date _____

Series, Parallel, and Series/Parallel Connections

Identify each circuit part as a series, parallel, or series/parallel connection.

_____ **1.** Pushbutton 1 and pushbutton 2 in Circuit 1 are connected in ___.

_____ **2.** Pushbutton 1, pushbutton 2, and the doorbell in Circuit 1 are connected in ___.

_____ **3.** The doorbell and the front door pushbutton in Circuit 2 are connected in ___.

_____ **4.** The three pushbuttons in Circuit 3 are connected in ___.

_____ **5.** The forward pushbutton and the normally open F contact in Circuit 3 are connected in ___.

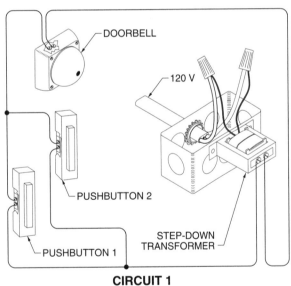

CIRCUIT 1

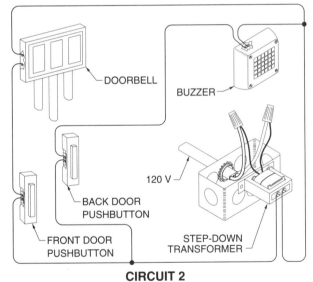

CIRCUIT 2

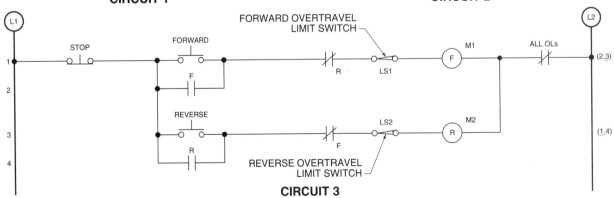

CIRCUIT 3

Electrical Tools and Test Instruments

Tech-Chek 2

Name _____ Date _____

Electrical Motor Controls

_____ 1. Tools may be organized using a(n) ___.
 A. pegboard   C. portable tool box
 B. tool pouch   D. all of the above

_____ 2. Electrical parts in the motor of a double insulated tool are surrounded by ___ to prevent electrical shock.

_____ 3. Ensure the switch is in the ___ position before connecting a tool to a power source.

_____ 4. A(n) ___ is used when checking voltage level and type.

_____ 5. A(n) ___ measures the current level in a circuit by measuring the strength of the magnetic field around a single conductor

_____ 6. A(n) ___ detects insulation deterioration by measuring high resistance values under high test voltages.

_____ 7. A(n) ___ is the best system for organizing tools to be used on the job or at a test bench.

_____ 8. Cutting tools should be ___.
 A. stainless steel   C. sharp and clean
 B. new   D. well used

_____ 9. All power tools should be grounded unless they are ___.

_____ 10. A change in sound during tool operation normally indicates ___.
 A. normal operation   C. the tool is in reverse
 B. trouble of some type   D. overheating

_____ 11. A(n) ___ scale is divided into unequally spaced segments.

_____ 12. A(n) ___ is a bar graph that displays a fraction of the full range on the graph.

_____ 13. A(n) ___ is an electromechanical device that indicates readings on a meter by the mechanical motion of a pointer.

_____ 14. ___ cutting pliers are used for cutting cable, removing knockouts, twisting wire, and deburring conduit.

_____ 15. ___ cutting pliers are used for cutting nails, wire, and rivets close to the workpiece.

_____ 16. A(n) ___ has solid-grip jaws and is usually constructed of nylon or laminated fiber.

_____ 17. High volume conduit installers generally use electric ___.

_____ **18.** A(n) ___ is ideal for pinpointing conduit, pipe, and ductwork locations.

_____ **19.** A(n) ___ is capable of measuring two or more electrical quantities.

_____ **20.** When reading an analog scale, the ___, ___, and ___ readings are added.

_____ **21.** A(n) ___ is used to display the shape of a voltage waveform.

_____ **22.** A(n) ___ is a voltage that appears on a meter not connected to a circuit.

_____ **23.** A(n) ___ is a test instrument that tests for a complete path for current to flow.

_____ **24.** A(n) ___ is a special DC voltmeter that detects the presence or absence of a signal.

_____ **25.** When using a receptacle tester, the ___ indicates whether the receptacle is wired correctly.

_____ **26.** ___ meters are less susceptible to electrical noise than ___ meters.

_____ **27.** A(n) ___ is a device used to determine phase sequence and open phases.

_____ **28.** The ___ switch on a digital logic probe sets the probe to detect short pulses.

_____ **29.** It is dangerous to use an adapter to plug a three-prong plug into a nongrounded receptacle unless a separate ___ is connected to an approved ground.

_____ **30.** A(n) ___ is a drill that rotates and drives simultaneously.

Analog Displays

_____ **1.** Nonlinear scale

_____ **2.** Secondary divisions

_____ **3.** Subdivisions

_____ **4.** Linear scale

_____ **5.** Primary divisions

Electrical Tools and Test Instruments

Name _____ Date _____

Tool Identification

_____ 1. Ball peen hammer

_____ 2. Chain wrench

_____ 3. Slip-joint pliers

_____ 4. Adjustable wrench

_____ 5. Phillips screwdriver

_____ 6. Flathead screwdriver

_____ 7. Locking pliers

_____ 8. Hex key wrench

_____ 9. Folding rule

_____ 10. Phillips offset screwdriver

Electrical Tools and Test Instruments

Worksheet 2-2

Name _____ Date _____

Electrical Tool Identification

_____ 1. Power cable cutter

_____ 2. Fuse puller

_____ 3. Conduit bender

_____ 4. Long-nose pliers

_____ 5. Side-cutting pliers

_____ 6. End-cutting pliers

_____ 7. Skinning knife

_____ 8. Reaming tool

_____ 9. Diagonal-cutting pliers

_____ 10. Wire stripper

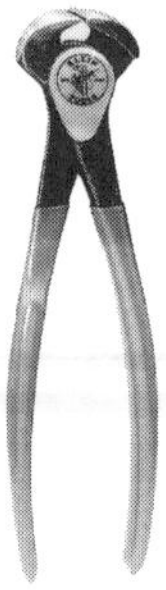

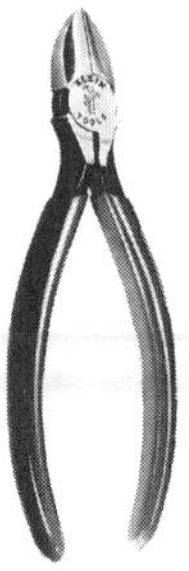

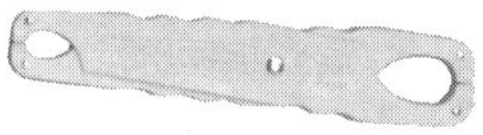

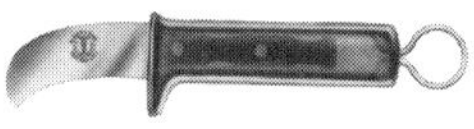

Ⓐ   Ⓑ   Ⓒ

Ⓓ

Ⓔ   Ⓕ   Ⓖ

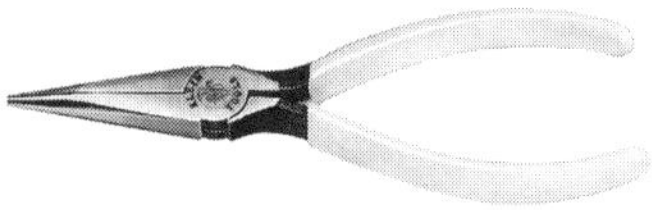

Ⓗ   Ⓘ   Ⓙ

Electrical Tools and Test Instruments

Worksheet 2-3

Name _____ Date _____

Analog Displays

List the correct reading for each function/range switch setting.

_____ **1.** Reading = ___ mA AC

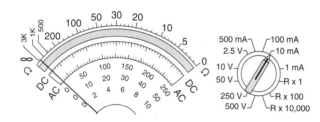

_____ **2.** Reading = ___ Ω

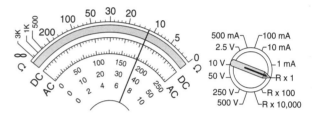

_____ **3.** Reading = ___ kΩ

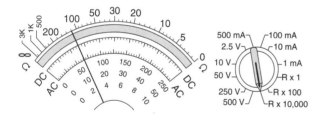

_____ **4.** Reading = ___ VAC

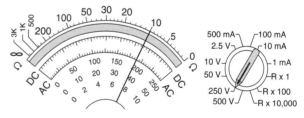

_____ **5.** Reading = ___ mA DC

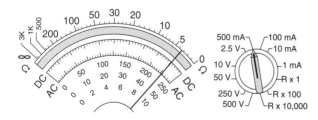

_____ **6.** Reading = ___ Ω

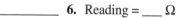

Electrical Safety

Tech-Chek 3

Name _____ Date _____

Electrical Motor Controls

_____ 1. Always remove the ___ side of a fuse first when removing fuses from circuits.

_____ 2. Class ___ fires consist of burning wood, clothing, or paper.

_____ 3. Class ___ fires consist of burning electrical equipment.

_____ 4. Class ___ fires consist of flammable liquids such as gasoline and oil.

_____ 5. Class ___ fires consist of burning combustible metals such as magnesium or aluminum.

_____ 6. A danger signal word on a warning sign is used to indicated a situation which ___.
   A. may result in minor or moderate injury
   B. could result in death or serious injury
   C. results in death or serious injury
   D. all of the above apply

_____ 7. Fuses should be installed ___ when replacing fuses.
   A. line side first
   B. load side first
   C. load and line side simultaneously
   D. with a screwdriver

_____ 8. Rags containing oil, gasoline, alcohol, shellac, paints, varnish, or lacquer must be ___.
   A. kept in a covered metal container
   B. stored in a wastebasket
   C. left out to dry
   D. stored in a cool, dry place

_____ 9. A(n) ___ is a confined space that has specific health and safety hazards associated with it.

_____ 10. An oxygen content of 12% to 14% by volume results in ___.

_____ 11. Lockout is the process of ___.

_____ 12. ___ is the connection of all exposed non-current-carrying metal parts to the earth.

_____ 13. A(n) ___ derived system is a system that supplies electrical power derived (taken from) transformers, storage batteries, solar photovoltaic systems, or generators.

_____ 14. A(n) ___ bonding jumper is a connection at the service equipment that connects the equipment grounding conductor, the grounding electrode conductor, and the grounded conductor (neutral conductor).

_____ **15.** A(n) ___ grounding conductor is an electrical conductor that provides a low-impedance ground path between electrical equipment and enclosures within the distribution system.

_____ **16.** A(n) ___ conductor is a conductor that has been intentionally grounded.

_____ **17.** A(n) ___ is a confined space that does not contain or have the potential to contain any hazards capable of causing death or serious physical harm.

_____ **18.** ___ rubber matting is specifically designed for use in front of open cabinets or high-voltage equipment.

_____ **19.** A danger tag is used alone only when ___.

_____ **20.** A paint spraybooth interior would be classified (under Article 500 of the NEC®) as ___.

Personal Protective Equipment

_____ **1.** Rubber insulating gloves

_____ **2.** Insulating matting

_____ **3.** Protective helmet

_____ **4.** Safety glasses

_____ **5.** Ear plugs

_____ **6.** Safety shoes

_____ **7.** Fire-resistant clothing

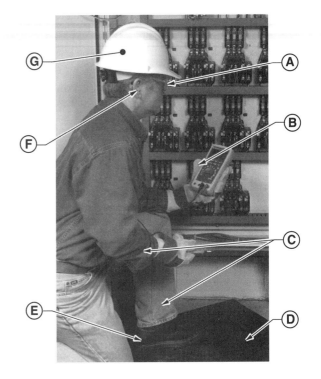

Electrical Safety

Worksheet 3-1

Name _____ Date _____

Lockout/Tagout

Determine if a lockout/tagout is required for each situation.

_____ **1.** Is lockout/tagout required for diagram 1?

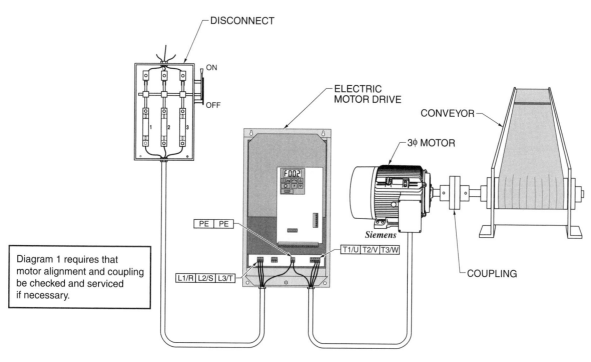

Diagram 1 requires that motor alignment and coupling be checked and serviced if necessary.

DIAGRAM 1

_____ **2.** Is lockout/tagout required for diagram 2?

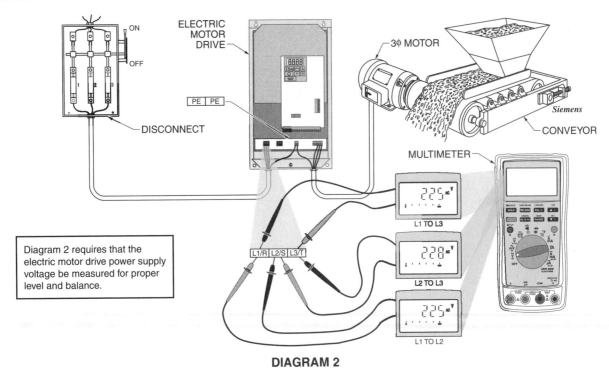

Diagram 2 requires that the electric motor drive power supply voltage be measured for proper level and balance.

DIAGRAM 2

_____ **3.** Is lockout/tagout required for diagram 3?

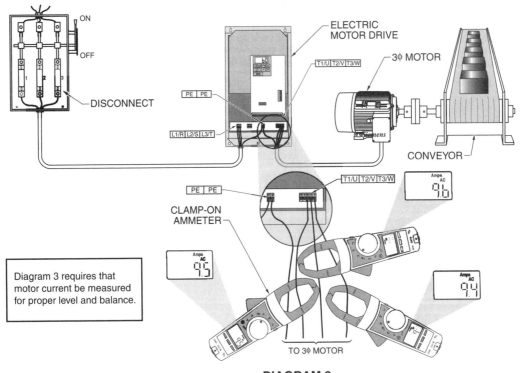

Diagram 3 requires that motor current be measured for proper level and balance.

DIAGRAM 3

_____ **4.** Is lockout/tagout required for diagram 4?

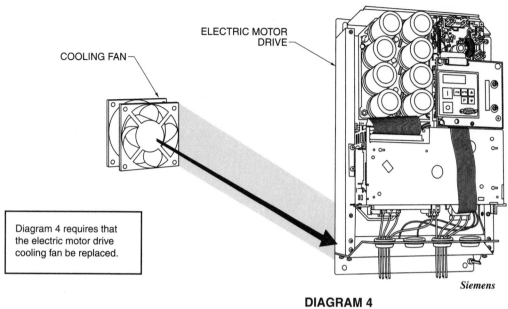

ELECTRIC MOTOR
DRIVE

COOLING FAN

Diagram 4 requires that
the electric motor drive
cooling fan be replaced.

Siemens

DIAGRAM 4

Electrical Safety

Worksheet 3-2

Name _____ Date _____

Fire Extinguisher Classes

_____ **1.** The class of fire at A is ___.

_____ **2.** The class of fire at B is ___.

_____ **3.** The class of fire at C is ___.

_____ **4.** The class of fire at D is ___.

_____ **5.** The class of fire at E is ___.

Ⓐ

Ⓑ

Ⓒ

Ⓓ

Ⓔ

Electrical Symbols and Diagrams

Tech-Chek 4

Name _____ Date _____

Electrical Motor Controls

_____ 1. A ___ drawing shows the physical details of an object as seen by the eye.
      A. pictorial   C. line
      B. schematic   D. wiring

_____ 2. In a line diagram, the power circuit is shown in ___ lines than the rest of the diagram.
      A. heavier   C. straighter
      B. thinner   D. none of the above

_____ 3. A ___ diagram is used to show the relationship between circuits and their corresponding components but not the actual location of the components.
      A. wiring   C. pictorial
      B. schematic   D. line

_____ 4. A pushbutton is an example of a(n) ___ control switch.
      A. manual   C. mechanical
      B. automatic   D. none of the above

_____ 5. A float switch is an example of a(n) ___ control switch.
      A. manual   C. mechanical
      B. automatic   D. none of the above

_____ 6. A line diagram is always read from ___ to ___.
      A. negative; positive   C. L1; L2
      B. right; left   D. L2; L1

_____ 7. In a line diagram, the overload contacts are shown as connected between the motor and ___.

_____ 8. A(n) ___ is a device that converts various forms of energy into electricity.

_____ 9. A ___ is used for remote control of devices.
      A. solenoid   C. contactor
      B. magnetic starter   D. all of the above

_____ 10. A(n) ___ is an electrical device which consists of a frame, plunger, and coil and is used to create a push or pull action.

_____ 11. A(n) ___ is an electrical device which consists of a frame, plunger, and coil and is used to open and close a set of contacts.

_____ 12. A(n) ___ is an electrical device which consists of a frame, plunger, and coil and is used to open and close a set of contacts in addition to providing overload protection.

_____ **13.** ___ contacts are used in the control circuit to form an electrical holding circuit.

_____ **14.** A(n) ___ diagram is a diagram that shows the electrical connections and functions of a specific circuit arrangement with graphic symbols.

_____ **15.** For consistency, the ___ symbol is always drawn in a line diagram after the motor.

_____ **16.** A(n) ___ is an assemblage of conductors and electrical devices through which current flows.

_____ **17.** Magnetic motor starter overloads have ___ which sense excessive current flow to the motor.

_____ **18.** ___ diagrams show, as closely as possible, the actual location of each component in a circuit.

_____ **19.** When troubleshooting electrical control circuits, the ___ circuit must be checked against the circuit diagram.

_____ **20.** A(n) ___ control circuit is a circuit that requires a person to initiate an action for the circuit to operate.

Device Identification

_____ **1.** Foot switch

_____ **2.** Silicon-controlled rectifier

_____ **3.** Normally closed limit switch

_____ **4.** Pilot light

_____ **5.** Solenoid

_____ **6.** Float switch

_____ **7.** 1φ motor

_____ **8.** 3φ motor

_____ **9.** Temperature switch

_____ **10.** Pressure or vacuum switch

_____ **11.** Flow switch

_____ **12.** Control transformer

_____ **13.** Motor starter

_____ **14.** Overload contacts

_____ **15.** Electrical connection

_____ **16.** Normally open pushbutton

Electrical Symbols and Diagrams

Worksheet 4-1

Name _____ Date _____

Electrical Symbols
Draw the appropriate symbol.

1. Normally open limit switch

2. Circuit breaker with thermal and magnetic overload

3. Normally open held-closed limit switch

4. Normally open and normally closed pushbutton

5. Single-voltage transformer

6. Dual-voltage transformer

7. 3ϕ motor

8. Normally open timed-closed contact

9. Disconnect

10. Two-position selector switch

11. Red pilot light

12. Photocell

13. Full-wave rectifier

14. Shunt field

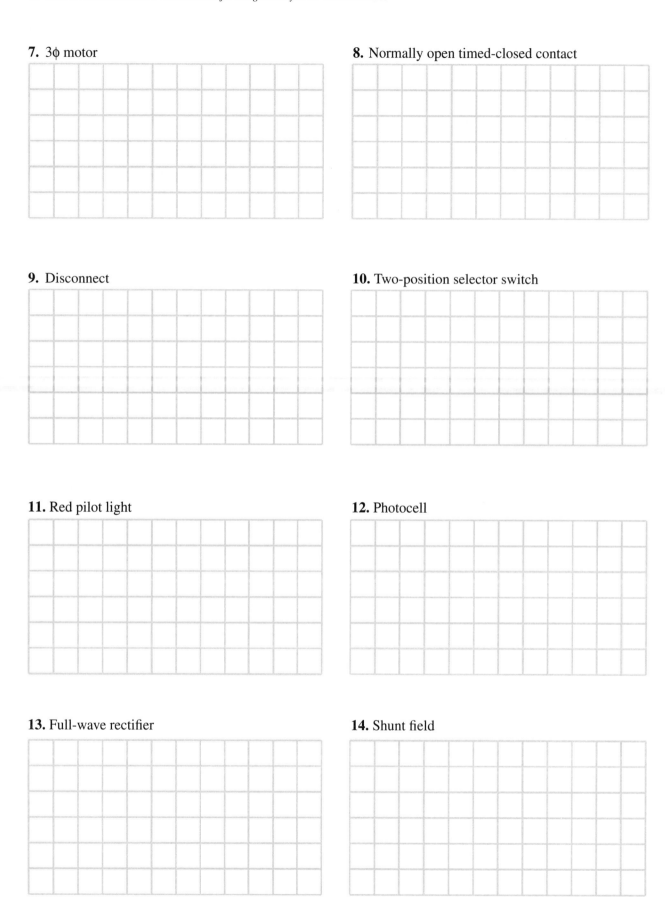

Electrical Symbols and Diagrams

Worksheet 4-2

Name _____   Date _____

Line Diagrams

Complete each line diagram with the appropriate symbol.

1. Normally closed held-open limit switch

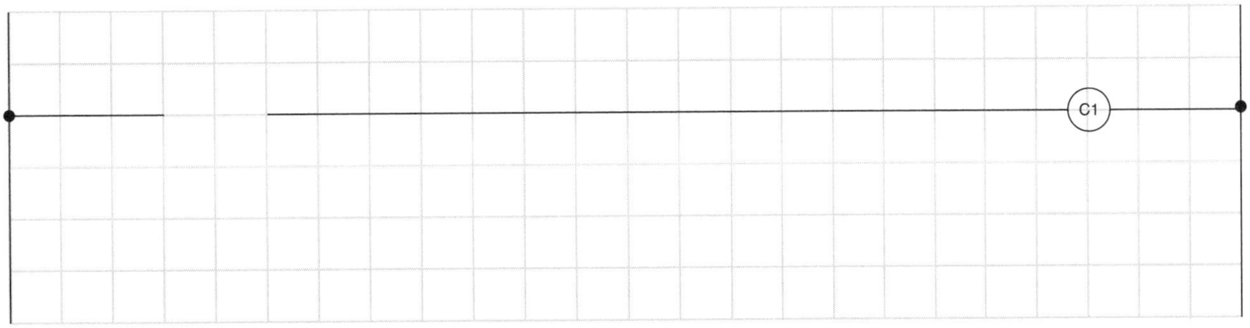

2. Normally closed timed-closed contact

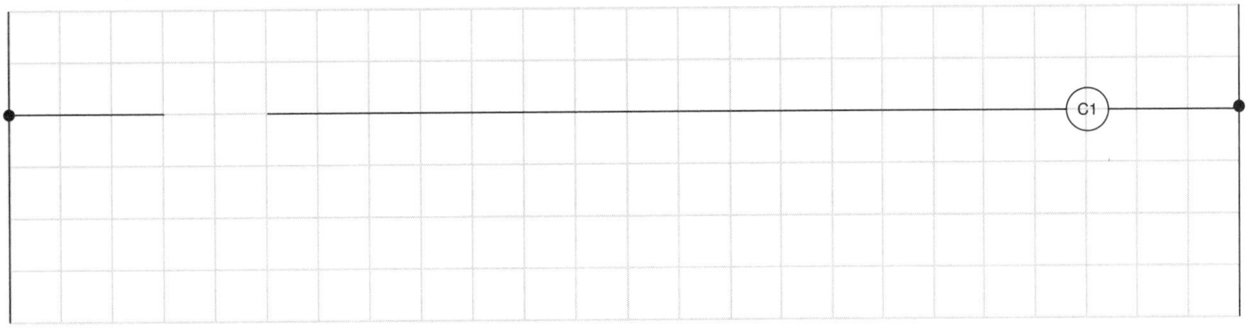

3. Normally closed mushroom head pushbutton

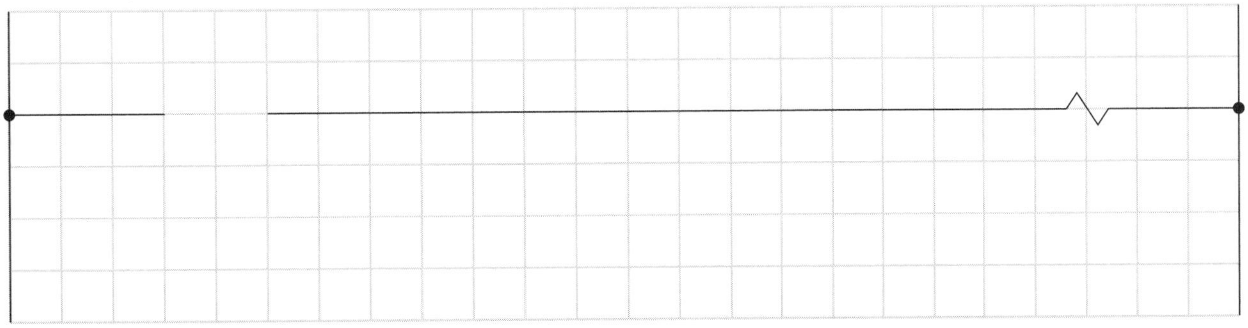

4. Normally open temperature-actuated switch

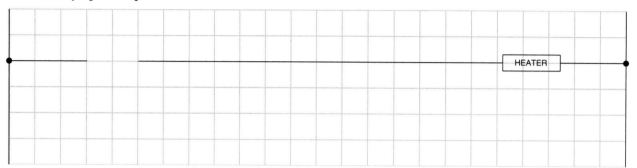

5. Normally open solid-state limit switch

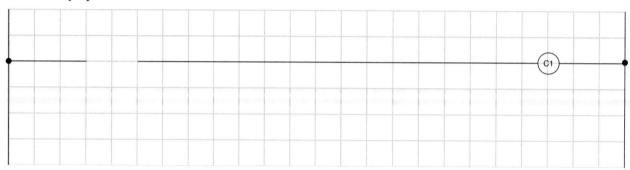

6. Normally closed flow switch

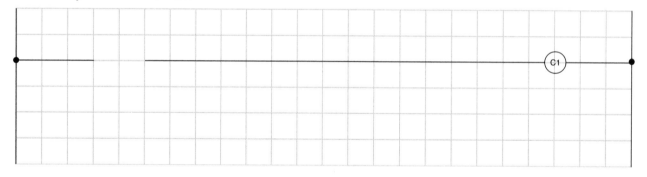

7. Thermal overload switch

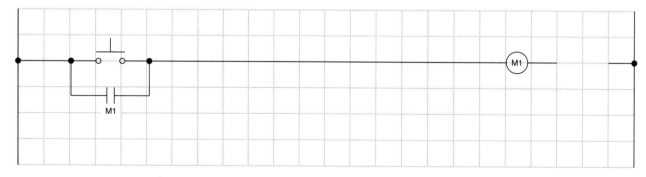

Electrical Symbols and Diagrams

Worksheet 4-3

Name _____ Date _____

Basic Circuit Design

Complete each line diagram according to the circuit information. Use standard lettering, numbering, and coding information.

1. Design a circuit in which a normally open start pushbutton controls a magnetic motor starter with three overload contacts.

CIRCUIT 1

2. Redraw Circuit 1, adding an auxiliary contact to form a memory circuit. Add a normally closed stop pushbutton to turn OFF the circuit.

CIRCUIT 2

3. Redraw Circuit 2, adding a foot switch and a limit switch that turn OFF the motor if actuated.

4. Design a control circuit in which a pressure switch is used to control a pump motor. The pump motor should turn ON any time the pressure drops below 30 psi.

Logic Applied to Line Diagrams

Tech-Chek 5

Name _____ Date _____

Electrical Motor Controls

_____ 1. Loads must be connected in ___ when more than one electrical load must be connected in a line diagram.

_____ 2. Control relays, solenoids, and pilot lights are loads connected directly to line ___.

_____ 3. A(n) ___ is a load that is connected indirectly to line 2 through overload contacts.

_____ 4. In a line diagram, pushbuttons, limit switches, and pressure switches are connected between line 1 and the ___.

_____ 5. ___ systems help to quickly identify the location and type of contacts controlled by a given device.

_____ 6. Each wire in a control circuit is assigned a(n) ___ to keep track of the different wires that connect the components in a circuit.

_____ 7. A control circuit is composed of three basic sections, which are the signal, decision, and ___ sections.

_____ 8. The ___ section of a control circuit starts or stops the flow of current by closing or opening the control device contacts.

_____ 9. The ___ section of a control circuit determines what work is to be done and in what order the work is to occur.

_____ 10. The ___ section of a circuit causes work to take place.

_____ 11. A(n) ___ condition refers to any input into a circuit by a person.

_____ 12. A(n) ___ condition refers to any input into a circuit by some moving part.

_____ 13. A(n) ___ condition refers to any input into a circuit from changes in a system.

_____ 14. When applying the numerical cross-reference system, normally closed contacts are indicated as a number that is ___.

_____ 15. Start pushbuttons are connected in ___ when adding additional start pushbuttons to a standard start/stop motor control circuit.

_____ 16. Stop pushbuttons are connected in ___ when adding additional stop pushbuttons to a standard start/stop motor control circuit.

_____ 17. ___ logic is developed when normally closed contacts are connected in series.

_____ 18. ___ logic is developed when normally closed contacts are connected in parallel.

Logic Functions

_____ **1.** OR

_____ **2.** AND

_____ **3.** NOT

_____ **4.** NOR

_____ **5.** Memory

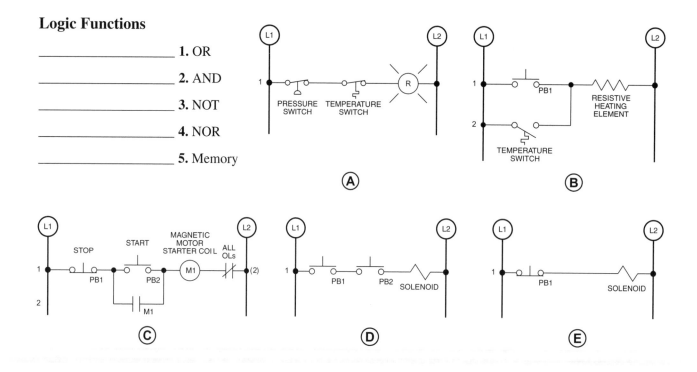

Reference Numbers

1. Add line-reference, numerical cross-reference, and wire-reference numbers per industrial standards.

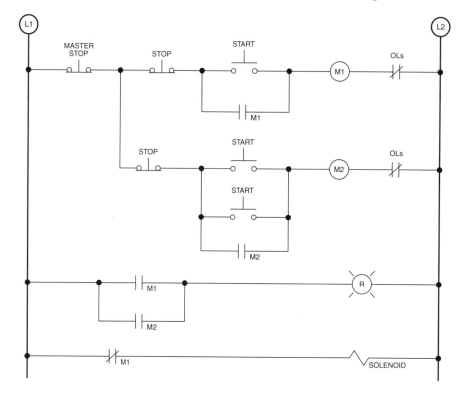

Logic Applied to Line Diagrams

Worksheet 5-1

Name _____   Date _____

Motor Starting with Memory

Use standard lettering, line-reference, and cross-reference numbering systems to complete each line diagram. Wire-reference numbers are not required. Note: *The motor starter includes both normally open and normally closed auxiliary contacts.*

1. Complete the control circuit line diagram so any one of three start pushbuttons starts the motor and any one of three stop pushbuttons stops the motor. Include memory so the motor remains running after any start pushbutton is pressed and released.

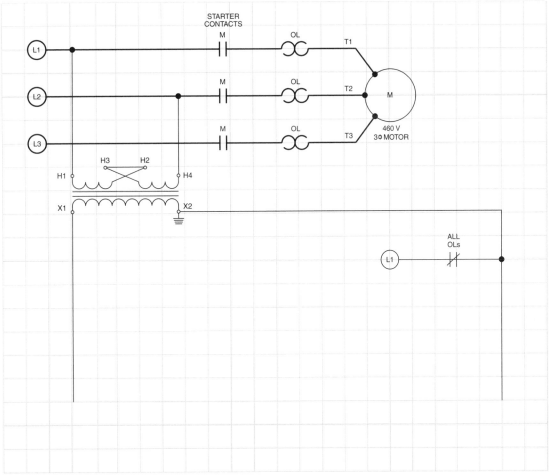

CIRCUIT 1

2. Redraw the control circuit line diagram of Circuit 1, adding red and green pilot lights. The red pilot light turns ON any time the motor is ON. The green pilot light turns ON any time the motor is OFF.

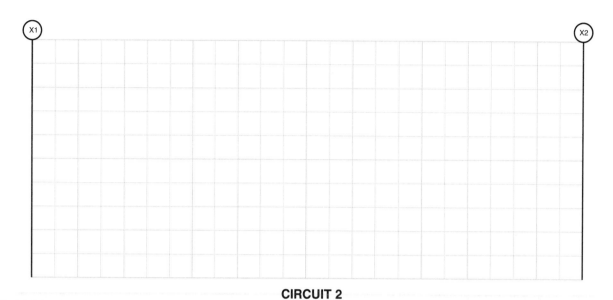

CIRCUIT 2

3. Redraw Circuit 2, adding a selector switch that is used to place the circuit in a jog or run position.

Logic Applied to Line Diagrams

Worksheet 5-2

Name _____ Date _____

Circuit Overload Protection

Use standard lettering, line-reference, and cross-reference numbering systems to complete each line diagram. Wire-reference numbers are not required. Note: *Assume that the motor starters have several normally open and normally closed auxiliary contacts.*

1. Draw the line diagram of three magnetic motor starters controlled by a common start/stop pushbutton station. Interconnect the three motor starters so if an overload occurs on any of the starters, all three are automatically disconnected. Design the circuit so Motor Starter 1 energizes Motor Starter 2 and Motor Starter 2 energizes Motor Starter 3.

CIRCUIT 1

2. Draw the line diagram of three magnetic motor starters controlled by three individual start/stop pushbutton stations. Include a Master Stop Pushbutton that stops all three starters when pressed. Design the circuit so the starters can be individually stopped by each start/stop pushbutton station when the Master Stop Pushbutton is not used. Each starter must have its own overload protection.

CIRCUIT 2

3. Redraw Circuit 2, adding a pressure switch that automatically stops all motors if excessive pressure is reached. Add a red pilot light that turns ON when Motor 1 is running, a green pilot light that turns ON when Motor 2 is running, and an amber pilot light that turns ON when Motor 3 is running.

Logic Applied to Line Diagrams

Worksheet 5-3

Name _____   Date _____

Multiple Conveyor Control

Use standard lettering, line-reference, and cross-reference numbering systems to complete each line diagram. Wire-reference numbers are not required. Note: *The motor starters include both normally open and normally closed contacts in any number required to solve the problem.*

1. Complete the line diagram of a control circuit for a three-belt, three-motor conveyor system in which Conveyor A feeds bulk material to Conveyor B, Conveyor B feeds the material to Conveyor C, and Conveyor C dumps the material. To prevent material pileups and ensure safe operation, design the circuit so Conveyor A and Conveyor B cannot start unless Conveyor C starter is energized, Conveyor A cannot start unless Conveyor B starter is energized, and Conveyor A and Conveyor B stop if Conveyor C stops because of an overload. In addition, Conveyor A stops and Conveyor C continues to run if Conveyor B stops because of an overload. Conveyor B and Conveyor C continue to run if Conveyor A stops. Only one start and one stop pushbutton may be used to control the conveyor system. Include individual pilot lights to show which conveyors are running.

Logic Applied to Line Diagrams

Worksheet 5-4

Name _____   Date _____

Selector Switch Control

Use standard lettering, line-reference, and cross-reference numbering systems to complete each line diagram. Wire-reference numbers are not required. Note: *The motor starters include both normally open and normally closed contacts in any number required to solve the problems.*

1. Design a start/stop/jog control circuit using a selector switch to provide the jog/run function. In the jog position, the start pushbuttons control the jogging of the motor. In the run position, the circuit functions as a standard start/stop circuit with memory. Include a red pilot light that turns ON when the circuit is in the jog condition and a green pilot light that turns ON when the circuit is in the run condition.

2. Design a motor control circuit that includes a standard start/stop pushbutton station that controls a motor starter. Include a green push-to-test pilot light that is used to indicate when a starter is energized and when the testing of the bulb is enabled by simply pushing the color cap on the pushbutton. The starter must energize when testing the bulb.

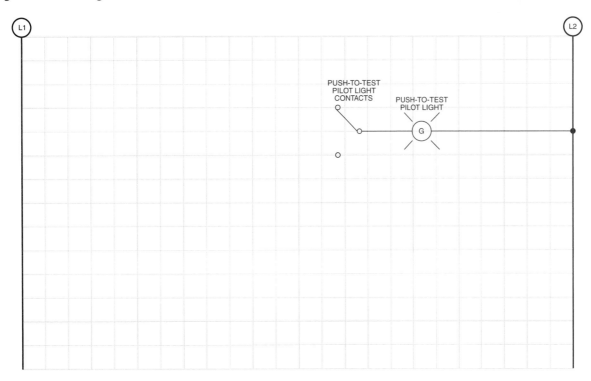

3. Design a circuit using two pushbuttons for NAND logic that control a solenoid. In addition, connect two limit switches for NOR logic that control a red pilot light.

Logic Applied to Line Diagrams

Worksheet 5-5

Name _____ Date _____

OR Circuit Logic

Use standard lettering, line-reference, and cross-reference numbering systems to complete each line diagram. Wire-reference numbers are not required.

1. Design an OR logic circuit in which one mechanical switch (limit), one manual switch (pushbutton), and two liquid level switches make up the signal section. The decision is OR logic and the action is a bell ringing and a red light ON simultaneously.

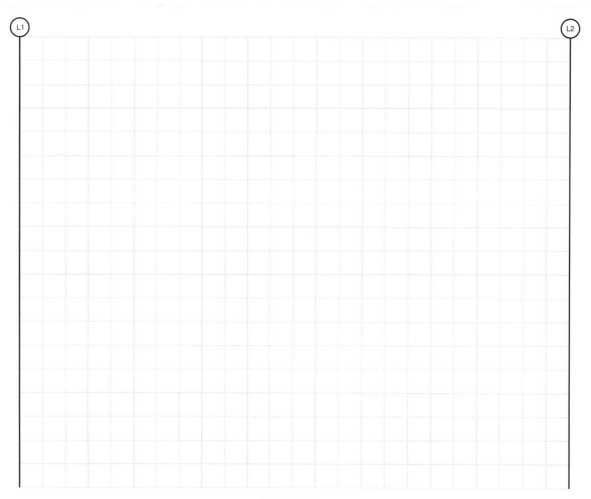

CIRCUIT 1

2. Develop a NOT logic circuit in which an automatic temperature control (temperature switch) is the signal, the decision is NOT logic, and the action is a red pilot light and a low-power heating element activated simultaneously.

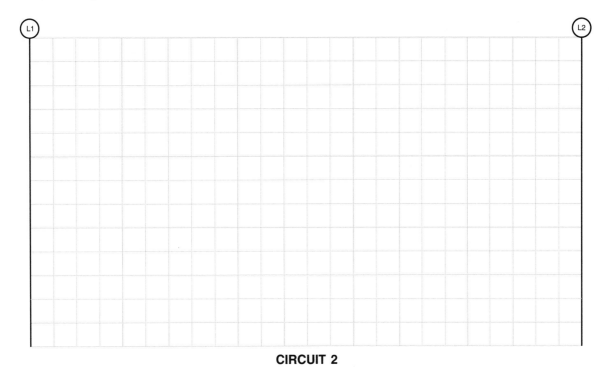

CIRCUIT 2

3. Redraw Circuit 2, adding a second temperature switch so either switch activates the loads when the temperature is below the set level. In addition, include a two-position selector switch that places the circuit in a system OFF or system ON position.

Logic Applied to Line Diagrams

Name _____ Date _____

AND/OR Combination Logic

Use standard lettering, line-reference, and cross-reference numbering systems to complete each line diagram. Wire-reference numbers are not required.

1. Design a circuit with AND/OR combination logic so the signal is manual (two pushbuttons and two limit switches), the decision is AND/OR combination logic so at least three devices must be actuated, and the action is a siren and a red light activated simultaneously.

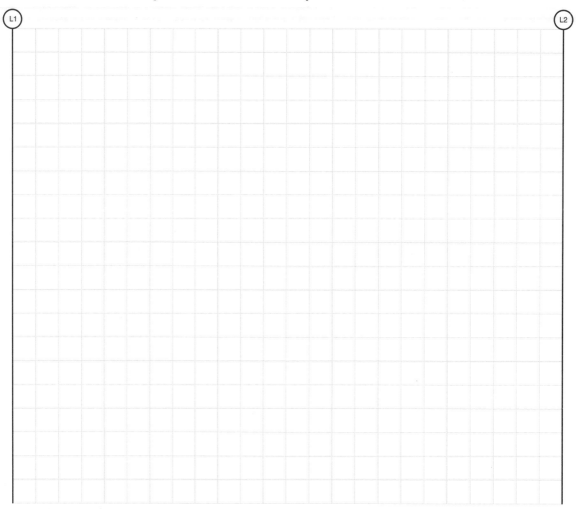

CIRCUIT 1

2. Design a circuit so the signal is automatic (vacuum switch) and manual (pushbutton); the decision is memory, so a pushbutton starts the operation and holds until a vacuum switch stops the operation; and the action is a magnetic starter coil and a red pilot light that indicates when the motor is energized.

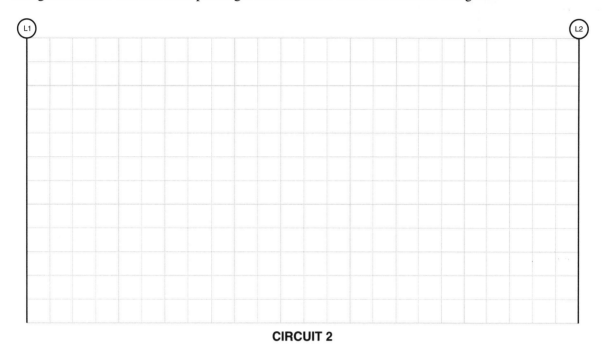

CIRCUIT 2

3. Redraw Circuit 2, adding a red pilot light that indicates when the motor is energized and a second pushbutton that stops the motor any time it is running.

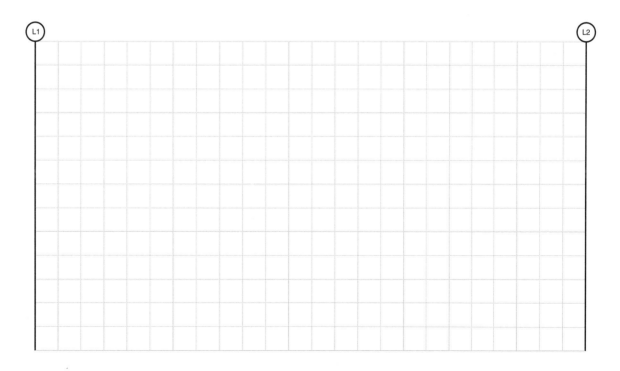

Logic Applied to Line Diagrams

Worksheet 5-7

Name _____ Date _____

Circuit Logic

Match each statement to the proper circuit. All circuits have been drawn with a light (L) to represent the load, whether it is a motor, bell, light, or any other load. In addition, each switch is illustrated as a pushbutton whether it is a maintained switch, momentary contact switch, pushbutton, switch-ON target, or any other type of switch.

_____ **1.** The warning light outside a darkroom (DO NOT ENTER) is OFF when the white light in the darkroom is ON. The warning light outside is ON when the white light in the darkroom is OFF.

_____ **2.** Switches are connected so the canopy of an airplane is ejected first and the pilot second regardless of which switch the pilot activates first.

_____ **3.** Two guns are connected to individual targets by switches so when two people compete in firing the guns, the fastest to fire is shown.

_____ **4.** Switches are connected so several people are required to fire a missile.

_____ **5.** An indicating light is ON to warn of danger when an oven is ON.

_____ **6.** A security guard monitoring a light panel can tell if the front door, back door, or both doors are open.

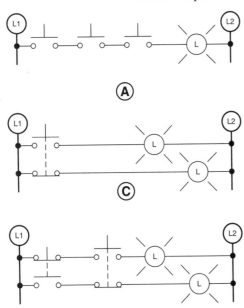

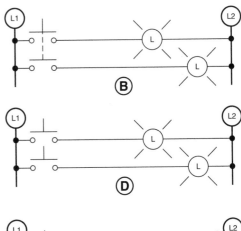

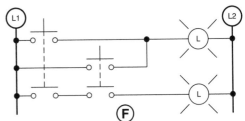

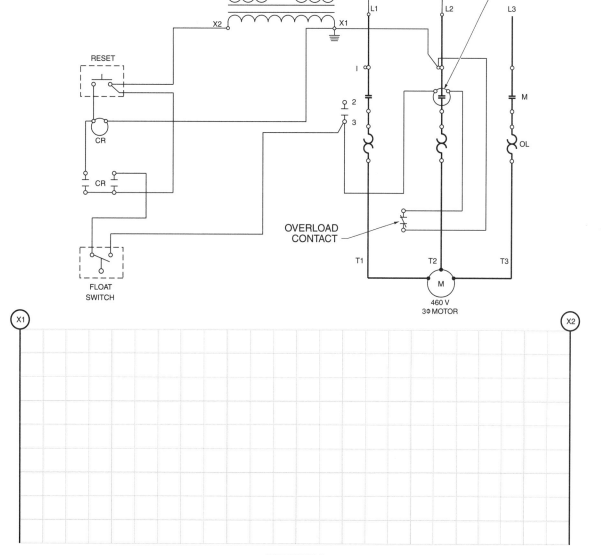

Circuit Wiring - 1ϕ Motor

1. Draw the line diagram that shows the logic of the control circuit. Use standard lettering, numbering, and coding information.

CIRCUIT 1

2. Redraw Circuit 1 adding a pressure switch that automatically stops the motor if pressure increases too high.

CIRCUIT 2

3. Redraw Circuit 2 adding a pilot light that indicates the motor is energized.

![Logic Applied to Line Diagrams — Worksheet 5-9]

Worksheet 5-9

Name _____ Date _____

Circuit Wiring – Remote Pushbutton Station

1. Draw the line diagram that shows the logic of the control circuit. Use standard lettering, numbering, and coding information.

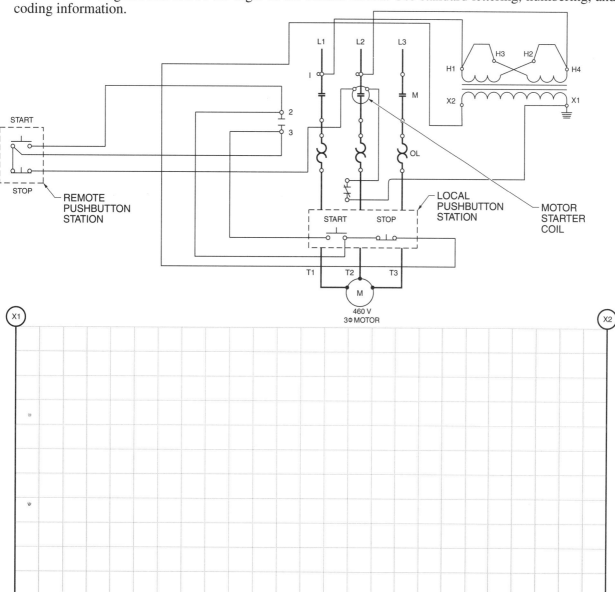

CIRCUIT 1

2. Redraw Circuit 1 adding a third remote start pushbutton that starts the motor.

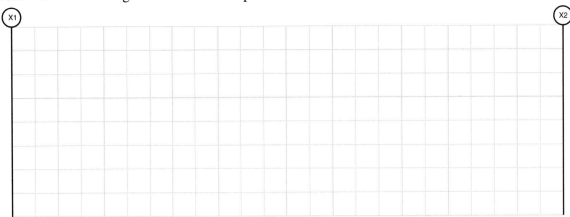

CIRCUIT 2

3. Redraw Circuit 2 adding a third remote stop pushbutton that stops the motor.

CIRCUIT 3

4. Redraw Circuit 3 adding a two-position (jog/run) selector switch. When the selector switch is in the jog position, the three start pushbuttons jog the motor.

Worksheet 5-10

Name _____ Date _____

Basic Switching Logic

1. Add a second start button to the basic control circuit so Start Button 1 or Start Button 2 can be used to start a motor. Include a second stop button that is connected so that Stop Button 1 or Stop Button 2 can be used to stop the motor.

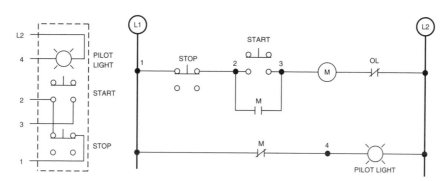

BASIC CONTROL CIRCUIT

BASIC CONTROL CIRCUIT WITH SECOND START BUTTON

2. Add a pressure switch to the basic control circuit to automatically stop the motor when the pressure in the system exceeds a setpoint pressure. Include a temperature switch to automatically stop the motor when the temperature in the system exceeds a set temperature.

BASIC CONTROL CIRCUIT WITH PRESSURE AND TEMPERATURE SWITCHES

3. Add a fuse to the basic control circuit with a pressure switch to automatically stop the motor when the fuse blows or the overload trips. Include an emergency start button to manually start the motor even when all the other buttons and switches are open (except the overload contacts or fuse). This allows for a manual start even when the temperature and/or pressure is above the setpoint.

BASIC CONTROL CIRCUIT WITH PRESSURE SWITCH AND FUSE

Solenoids, DC Generators, and DC Motors

Tech-Chek 6

Name _____ Date _____

Electrical Motor Controls

_____ **1.** The strength of an electromagnet can be increased by ___.
    A. increasing the voltage   C. inserting an iron core
    B. increasing the number of   D. all of the above
       turns of wire

_____ **2.** A(n) ___ is the number of locations within the valve in which the spool is placed to direct fluid through the valve.

_____ **3.** A small air gap is left in the iron core armature circuit to ___.
    A. prevent eddy currents   C. reduce cost
    B. prevent the armature from   D. prevent heat buildup in the armature
       staying in a sealed position   circuit

_____ **4.** Voltage should be at least ___ % of a solenoid's rated value.

_____ **5.** Without the ___, excessive noise, wear, and heat build up on the armature faces.

_____ **6.** ___ magnets are magnets that can retain their magnetism after a magnetizing force has been removed.

_____ **7.** ___ magnets are magnets that have extreme difficulty in retaining any magnetism after the magnetizing force has been removed.

_____ **8.** A burned out solenoid is normally evident by ___.

_____ **9.** A DC generator always has a(n) ___ armature and ___ field windings.

_____ **10.** The ___ is the relationship between the current in a conductor and the magnetic field existing around the conductor.

_____ **11.** The output voltage of a shunt-wound generator may be controlled by means of a(n) ___ connected in series with the shunt field.

_____ **12.** The ___ theory of magnetism states that all substances are made up of an infinite number of molecular magnets.

_____ **13.** A(n) ___ is an magnetic laminate assembly consisting of a coil of wire and a source of voltage.

_____ **14.** The ___ is used to determine the direction of motion of a current-carrying conductor in a magnetic field.

_____ **15.** ___ is unwanted current induced in the metal structure of a device.

_____ **16.** A(n) ___ is a single turn of conducting material mounted on the face of the magnetic laminate assembly or armature.

_____ **17.** The mechanical life of most coils is improved by encapsulating them in ___ or a glass-reinforced alkyd material.

_____ **18.** ___ voltage is the minimum control voltage which causes the armature to start to move.

_____ **19.** ___ voltage is the voltage which exists when the voltage has reduced sufficiently to allow the solenoid to open.

_____ **20.** Manufacturers provide letter or ___ codes to indicate the voltages available for a given solenoid.

_____ **21.** ___ two-way valves are common in refrigeration equipment.

_____ **22.** DC series motors can develop ___ of full-load torque upon starting.

_____ **23.** A solenoid ___ when the voltage is excessive.

_____ **24.** ___ voltages may damage the insulation on the solenoid coil.

_____ **25.** No movement of the needle on an analog meter or infinite resistance on a(n) ___ meter indicates the coil is open and defective.

_____ **26.** ___ valves are used as shutoff, check, or quick-exhaust valves.

_____ **27.** A(n) ___ motor uses magnets rather than a coil of wire for the field windings.

_____ **28.** A(n) ___ circuit is a circuit in which current leaves its normal path and travels to the frame of the motor.

_____ **29.** A(n) ___ motor has the advantage of high torque and constant speed.

_____ **30.** A(n) ___ connects a brush to the external circuit of a DC motor.

Solenoid Identification

_____ **1.** Vertical-action

_____ **2.** Horizontal-action

_____ **3.** Clapper

_____ **4.** Bell-crank

_____ **5.** Plunger

(A)

(B)

(C)

(D)

(E)

Solenoids, DC Generators, and DC Motors

Worksheet 6-1

Name _____ Date _____

Pushbutton Circuit Control

Complete the line diagram of the cylinder control circuit. Use standard lettering, numbering, and coding information.

1. Draw the line diagram of the control circuit using one pushbutton (PB1) to control the advance of the cylinder and another pushbutton (PB2) to control the retracting of the cylinder.

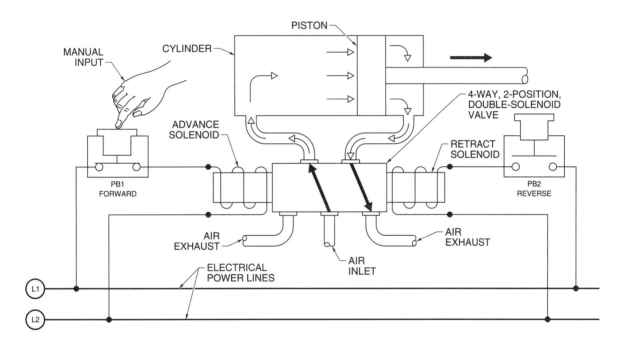

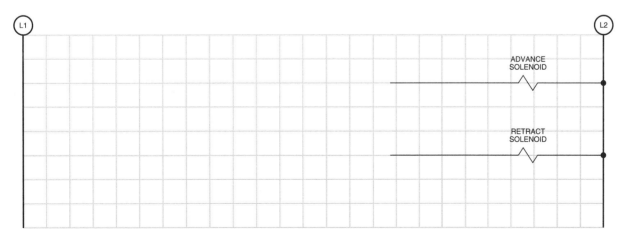

Solenoids, DC Generators, and DC Motors

Worksheet 6-2

Name _____ Date _____

Manual Control Circuit with Memory

Complete the line diagram of the cylinder control circuit. Use standard lettering, numbering, and coding information.

1. Complete the line diagram so the cylinder advances when PB1 is pressed and released. Include a limit switch that automatically returns the cylinder when the cylinder is fully advanced. *Note:* A contactor which is capable of controlling normally open and normally closed contacts is provided in parallel with the solenoid. The contactor can be used to add circuit memory.

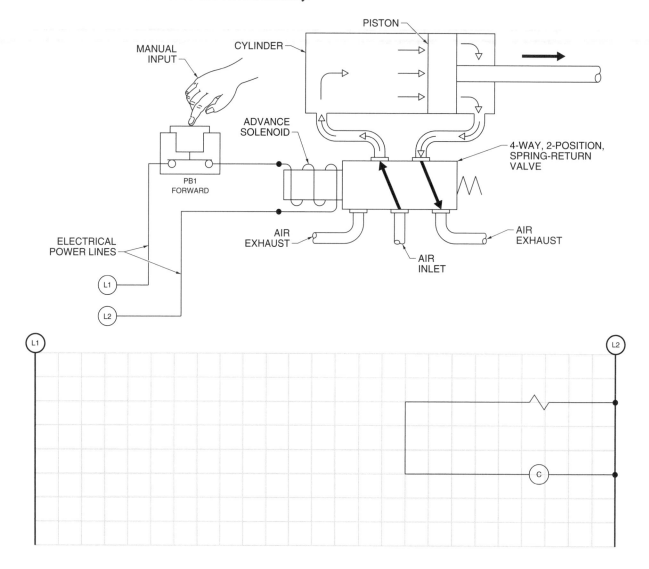

Solenoids, DC Generators, and DC Motors

Worksheet 6-3

Name _____ Date _____

Automatic Circuit Control

Complete the line diagram of the cylinder control circuit. Use standard lettering, numbering, and coding information.

1. Complete the line diagram so PB1 and a foot switch advance the cylinder and PB2 or a limit switch retracts the cylinder.

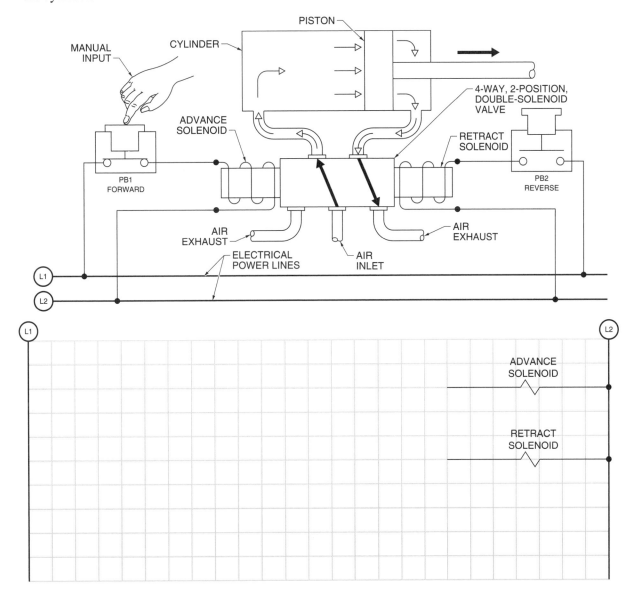

Solenoids, DC Generators, and DC Motors

Worksheet 6-4

Name _____ Date _____

Manual Override Circuit Control

Complete the line diagram of the cylinder control circuit. Use standard lettering, numbering, and coding information.

1. Design the circuit so the cylinder advances only if two pushbuttons (PB1 and PB2) are pressed. Add a contactor that automatically returns the cylinder. Include a manual return pushbutton (PB3) to manually return the cylinder if the pressure falls below the setting of the pressure switch.

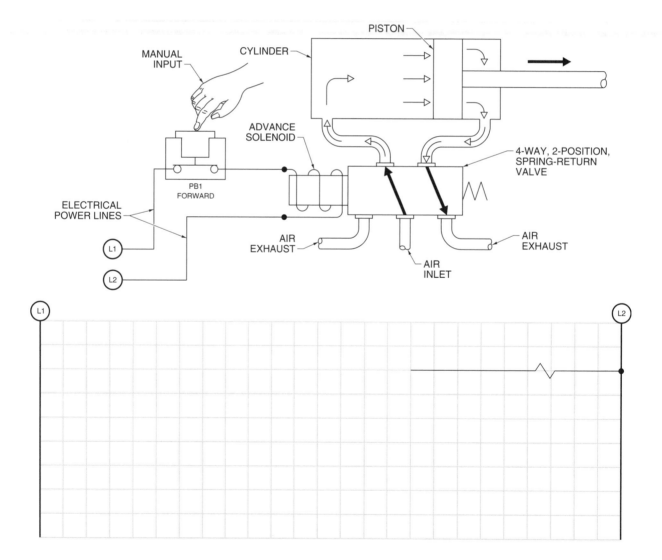

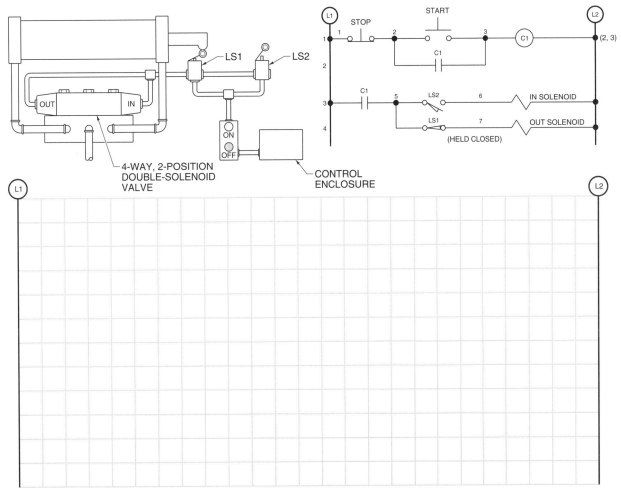

Solenoids, DC Generators, and DC Motors

Worksheet 6-5

Name _____ Date _____

Selector Switch Circuit Control
Draw the line diagram of the cylinder control circuit. Use standard lettering, numbering, and coding information.

1. Add a selector switch to determine manual or automatic control of the cylinder. The cylinder cycles continuously and automatically back and forth when the selector switch is in the automatic position and the start pushbutton is pressed and released. The cycling stops when the stop pushbutton is pressed. The cylinder advances only when a pushbutton (PB1) is pressed and retracts only when a second pushbutton (PB2) is pressed when the selector switch is in the manual position. *Note:* Limit switch 1 (LS1) is normally open (held closed) because the cylinder is retracted. Assume that no memory is required for either solenoid.

CIRCUIT 1

2. Redraw Circuit 1, adding an emergency stop pushbutton that stops the solenoids from being energized in either the manual or automatic condition until a reset pushbutton is activated. The circuit includes six pushbuttons (start, stop, PB1, PB2, reset, and emergency stop), two limit switches, two solenoids, a selector switch, and two contactors.

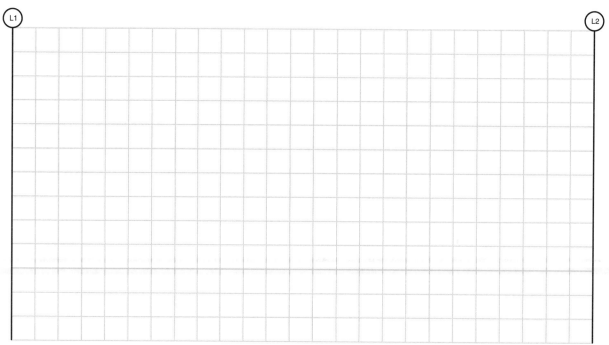

CIRCUIT 2

3. Redraw Circuit 2, adding a red light to indicate when the in solenoid is energized, a green light to indicate when the out solenoid is energized, and a yellow light to indicate when the emergency stop is pressed.

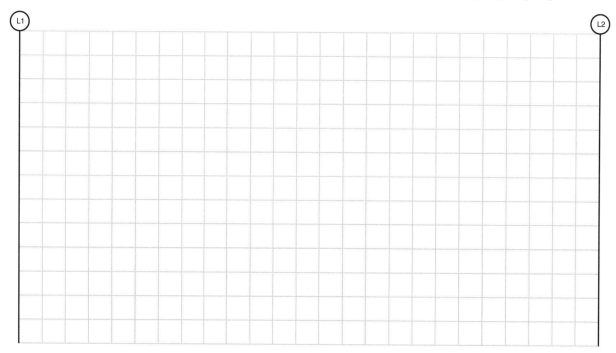

Solenoids, DC Generators, and DC Motors

Worksheet 6-6

Name _____   Date _____

Solenoid in a Lubrication System

1. Draw the line diagram so lubricant is dispensed every time the pushbutton is pressed and held, and a two-position selector switch is in the hand position.

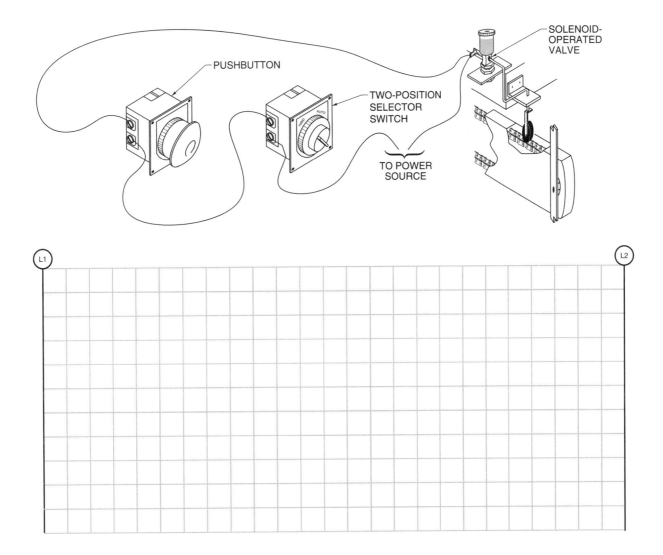

Solenoids, DC Generators, and DC Motors

Worksheet 6-7

Name _____ Date _____

DC Motor Leads

1. Mark each motor lead as A1, A2, S1, S2, etc.

2. Mark each motor lead as A1, A2, S1, S2, etc.

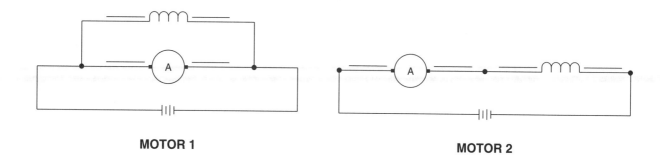

MOTOR 1

MOTOR 2

3. Mark each motor lead as A1, A2, S1, S2, etc.

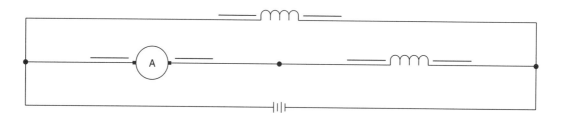

MOTOR 3

Motor Identification

_____ **1.** Motor 1 is a(n) ___ motor.

_____ **2.** Motor 2 is a(n) ___ motor.

_____ **3.** Motor 3 is a(n) ___ motor.

AC Generators, Transformers, and AC Motors

Tech-Chek 7

Name _____ Date _____

Electrical Motor Controls

_____ 1. In a transformer, the ___ winding is the coil that draws power from the source.

_____ 2. In a transformer, the ___ winding is the coil that delivers the energy at a transformed or changed voltage to a load.

_____ 3. Step-up or step-down, when used with transformers, always refer to ___.

_____ 4. A(n) ___ is an electrical interface designed to change AC from one voltage level to another.

_____ 5. ___ are magnets used to produce the magnetic field in a generator.

_____ 6. A(n) ___ is a decrease to 0 V on one or more power lines lasting from 0.5 cycles up to 3 sec.

_____ 7. A(n) ___ is a decrease to 0 V on one or more power lines lasting for more than 3 sec up to 1 min.

_____ 8. UPS stands for ___.
    A. unplanned power surge   C. utility power substation
    B. underground piping system   D. uninterruptible power system

_____ 9. A(n) ___ is a transformer that is used to step down the voltage to the control circuit of a system or machine.

_____ 10. The ___ is a measure of the amount of energy required to realign the iron atoms in the core of a transformer.

_____ 11. The heat produced by ___ represents a loss because it does no useful work.

_____ 12. A(n) ___ is a connection brought out of a winding at a point between its endpoints to allow changing the voltage or current ratio.

_____ 13. Two methods that are used to determine if a transformer has failed are ___ and ___.

_____ 14. ___ is the simplest method used to start a 1ϕ motor.

_____ 15. A starting winding is also known as a(n) ___.

_____ 16. ___ is the opposition to the flow of alternating current in a circuit due to inductance.

_____ 17. A(n) ___ motor is the most common motor used in industrial applications.

_____ 18. A(n) ___ motor is a motor that has no physical electrical connection to the rotor.

_____ **19.** The two most common motor enclosures are ___ enclosures and ___ enclosures.

_____ **20.** A bad motor is usually replaced, rather than repaired, if the horsepower is ___ or less.

_____ **21.** ___ is a medium in which an electric field is maintained with little or no outside energy supply.

_____ **22.** A(n) ___ capacitor is formed by winding two sheets of aluminum foil separated by pieces of thin paper impregnated with an electrolyte.

_____ **23.** When using a DMM to measure the resistance of two coils in series, the total resistance is ___ the resistance of one coil.

_____ **24.** When using a DMM to measure the resistance of two coils in parallel, the total resistance is ___ the resistance of one coil.

_____ **25.** A(n) ___ is a conducting medium in which the current flow occurs by ion migration.

_____ **26.** A(n) ___ is a connection that has each coil end connected end-to-end to form a closed loop.

_____ **27.** A(n) ___ is a connection that has one end of each coil connected together and the other end of each coil left open for connection to the load.

_____ **28.** A(n) ___ is a decrease to 0 V on all power lines for a period of more than 1 min.

_____ **29.** ___ voltages are normally erratic, large voltages or spikes that have a short duration and a short rise time.

_____ **30.** When the ratio of primary coils to secondary coils on a transformer is 1:2, the transformer is known as a(n) ___ transformer.

Transformers

_____ **1.** The primary side voltage is ___ V.

_____ **2.** The primary side current is ___ A .

_____ **3.** The secondary side current is ___ A.

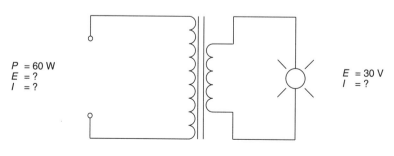

$P = 60$ W
$E = ?$
$I = ?$

$E = 30$ V
$I = ?$

TRANSFORMER RATIO = 4 TO 1

AC Generators, Transformers, and AC Motors

Worksheet 7-1

Name _____ Date _____

Delta-to-Delta Connections
Complete the transformer wiring diagram in a delta-to-delta transformer bank connection.

1. Connect the primary transformer lines to the distribution system to form a delta-connected primary. Connect the secondary transformer lines to the distribution system to provide 3ϕ, high-voltage 1ϕ, and low-voltage 1ϕ power. Connect each load to the correct power supply.

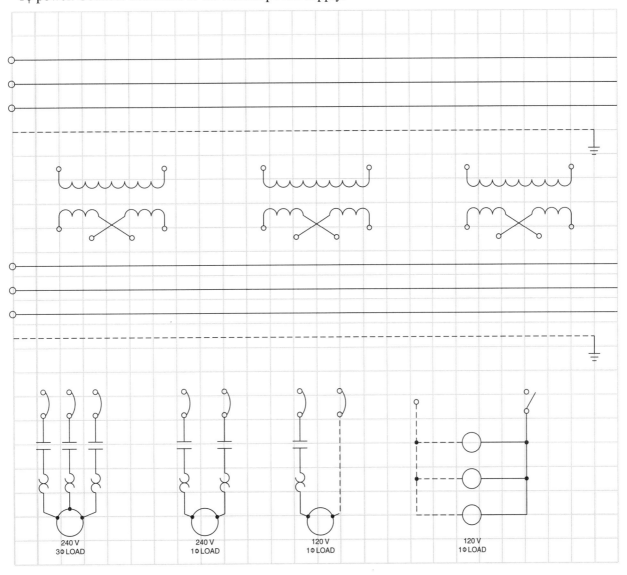

| 240 V
3ϕ LOAD | 240 V
1ϕ LOAD | 120 V
1ϕ LOAD | 120 V
1ϕ LOAD |

AC Generators, Transformers, and AC Motors

Worksheet 7-2

Name _____ Date _____

Wye-to-Wye Connections

Complete the transformer wiring diagram in a wye-to-wye transformer bank connection.

1. Connect the primary transformer lines to the distribution system to form a wye-connected primary. Connect the secondary transformer lines to the distribution system to form a wye-connected secondary that provides 3ϕ, high-voltage 1ϕ, and low-voltage 1ϕ power. Connect each load to the correct power supply.

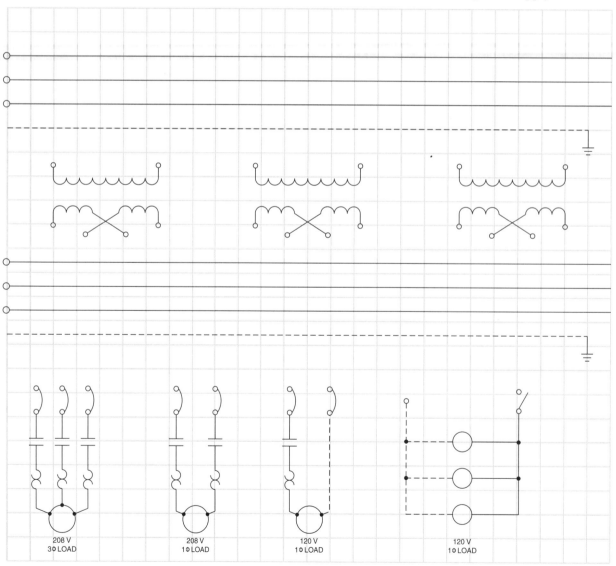

AC Generators, Transformers, and AC Motors

Worksheet 7-3

Name _____ Date _____

Delta-to-Wye Connections
Complete the transformer wiring diagram in a delta-to-wye transformer bank connection.

1. Connect the primary transformer lines to the distribution system to form a delta-connected primary. Connect the secondary transformer lines to the distribution system to form a wye-connected secondary that provides 3ϕ, high-voltage 1ϕ, and low-voltage 1ϕ power. Connect each load to the correct power supply.

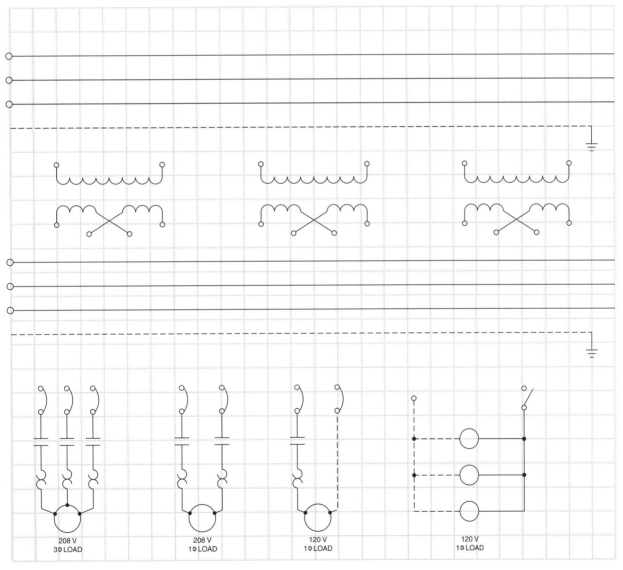

AC Generators, Transformers, and AC Motors

Worksheet 7-4

Name _____ Date _____

Wye-to-Delta Connections

Complete the transformer wiring diagram in a wye-to-delta transformer bank connection.

1. Connect the primary transformer lines to the distribution system to form a delta-connected secondary that provides 3ϕ, high-voltage 1ϕ, and low-voltage 1ϕ power. Connect each load to the correct power supply.

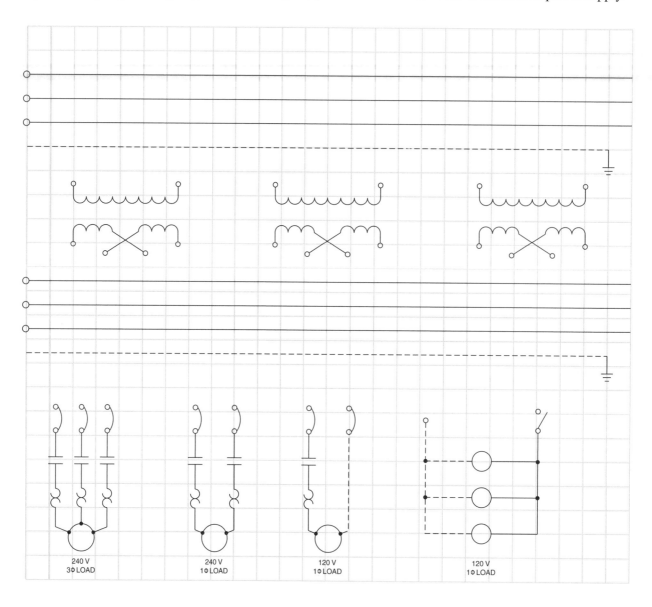

| 240 V 3ϕ LOAD | 240 V 1ϕ LOAD | 120 V 1ϕ LOAD | 120 V 1ϕ LOAD |

AC Generators, Transformers, and AC Motors

Worksheet 7-5

Name _____   Date _____

Dual-Voltage Control Transformer Installation

1. Draw the line diagram that shows the logic of the control circuit. Use standard lettering, numbering, and coding information.

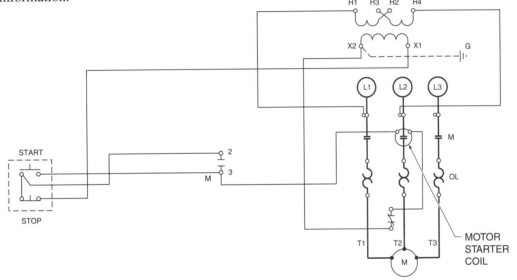

AC Generators, Transformers, and AC Motors

Worksheet 7-6

Name _____ Date _____

Motor Leads

1. Mark each motor lead as T1, T2, etc.

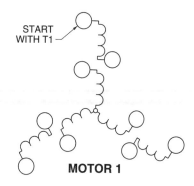

MOTOR 1

2. Mark each motor lead as T1, T2, etc.

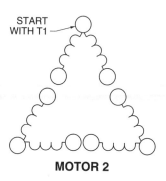

MOTOR 2

Motor Identification

_____ **1.** Motor 1 is a(n) ___ motor.

_____ **2.** Motor 2 is a(n) ___ motor.

Contactors and Motor Starters

Tech-Chek 8

Name _____   Date _____

Electrical Motor Controls

_____ 1. When motors were first introduced, they were started and stopped by ___.
A. magnetic motor starters   C. knife switches
B. magnetic contactors   D. solenoid switches

_____ 2. One of the advantages of using a double-break contact instead of a single-break contact is that a double-break contact ___.
A. has a higher contact   C. has a higher contact rating when enclosed
   rating in a smaller space   in a steel case
B. is not made of soft copper   D. does not present an electrical hazard

_____ 3. Copper contacts have been replaced with ___ alloy contacts because of the problems of using copper with knife switches.

_____ 4. A(n) ___ diagram shows the connection and placement of an installation or its component devices or parts.

_____ 5. ___ interlocked contactors are two contactors that are connected in such a way that both sets of contacts cannot be closed at the same time.

_____ 6. Manual starters are selected based on phasing, number of poles, voltage, starter size, and ___.

_____ 7. A(n) ___ is a condition that occurs when a motor is loaded so heavily that the motor shaft cannot turn.

_____ 8. The three stages that a motor must go through in normal operation are resting, starting, and ___.

_____ 9. Fuses or ___ are used to protect a motor against very high currents, short circuits, or a ground fault.

_____ 10. A 120 V, 1ϕ power source has one hot wire and ___ neutral wire(s).

_____ 11. A 230 V, 1ϕ power source has two hot wires and ___ neutral wire(s).

_____ 12. A 3ϕ power source has ___ hot wire(s) and zero neutral wires.

_____ 13. A(n) ___ is a device that is used only periodically to remove electrical circuits from their supply source.

_____ 14. Manual contactors are normally used with ___ circuits and resistance loads.

_____ 15. The main device in an overload relay is the ___.

_____ **16.** A manual starter is a(n) ___ with an added overload protection device.

_____ **17.** Overload protection devices are required by the ___.

_____ **18.** ___ temperature is the temperature of the air surrounding a motor.

_____ **19.** A(n) ___ alloy is a metal that has a fixed temperature at which it changes directly from a solid to a liquid state.

_____ **20.** A starter may be reset after a(n) ___ is removed.

_____ **21.** Enclosures provide ___ and electrical protection for the operator and the starter.

_____ **22.** A(n) ___ is a control device that uses pushbuttons to energize or de-energize the load connected to it.

_____ **23.** ___ contacts are contacts that break the electrical circuit in two places.

_____ **24.** A(n) ___ is a sensing device used to monitor the heat generated by excessive current and the heat created through ambient temperature rise.

_____ **25.** NEMA Type ___ enclosures are intended for indoor use primarily to provide a degree of protection against human contact with the enclosed equipment in locations where unusual service conditions do not exist.

_____ **26.** Manual motor starters are used in applications such as air compressors, conveyor systems, and ___.

_____ **27.** Manual contactors directly control ___ circuits.

_____ **28.** A(n) ___ overload measures the strength of the magnetic field around the wire instead of converting the current into heat.

_____ **29.** ___ power line(s) must be broken when using a contactor to control a 3φ load.
A. One   C. Three
B. Two   D. none of the above

_____ **30.** ___ arcs are the most difficult arcs to extinguish on a set of contacts.

_____ **31.** ___ are used to help confine, divide, and extinguish arcs for each set of contacts.
A. Arc chutes   C. Current transformers
B. Overloads   D. Transient suppression modules

_____ **32.** ___ are used to provide a magnetic field that helps move contacts apart as quickly as possible.
A. Silver contacts   C. Blow-out coils
B. Current transformers   D. Transient suppression modules

_____ **33.** The power rating of a contactor or motor starter ___ as the NEMA number (Size 1, 2, etc.) of the contactor or motor starter increases.
A. increases   C. remains the same
B. decreases   D. none of the above

_____ **34.** The current rating of a contactor or motor starter is the rating for ___.
A. each individual contact   C. 12 hr of operation
B. the whole contactor divided   D. the whole contactor
   by the number of contacts

_____ **35.** The main difference between a contactor and a motor starter is the addition of ___ to the motor starter.

_____ **36.** Two overload relays used to protect motors are thermal and ___ overload relays.

_____ **37.** Ambient temperature, full-load current rating, and ___ must be known when selecting the overloads for a motor starter.

_____ **38.** An inherent motor protector is designed to protect a motor from ___.

_____ **39.** ___ contactor assemblies may have several sets of contacts.

_____ **40.** ___ contactor assemblies are made of laminated steel.
      A. AC   C. Low-voltage
      B. DC   D. Static

_____ **41.** A(n) ___ is a device that dissipates the energy present across opening contacts.

_____ **42.** A(n) ___ relay is an overload relay which resets automatically.

_____ **43.** A(n) ___ is built into an overload device to indicate to the operator that an overload has taken place within the device.

_____ **44.** ___ are used on large motor starters to reduce the current flowing to the overload relay.

_____ **45.** As ambient temperature increases, ___ current is needed to trip overload devices.
      A. more   C. does not change
      B. less   D. none of the above

_____ **46.** ___ are overload devices located directly on or in a motor to provide overload protection.

_____ **47.** A(n) ___ performs the same function as a motor starter, but can also vary motor speed, reverse the motor, and display operating information.

_____ **48.** A(n) ___ is an electronic device that changes AC into DC.

_____ **49.** A(n) ___ is an electronic device that changes DC into AC.

_____ **50.** Article ___ of the NEC® covers the design and installation of electronic systems that contain motors, motor circuits, and motor controllers.

Contactors and Motor Starters

Worksheet 8-1

Name _____ Date _____

NEMA Enclosures

Determine the required NEMA enclosure for each location.

_____ **1.** Required enclosure is NEMA ___.

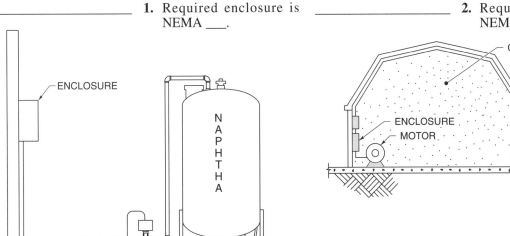

_____ **2.** Required enclosure is NEMA ___.

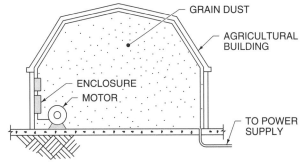

_____ **3.** Required enclosure is NEMA ___.

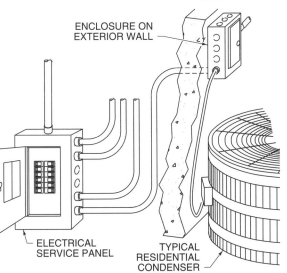

_____ **4.** Required enclosure is NEMA ___.

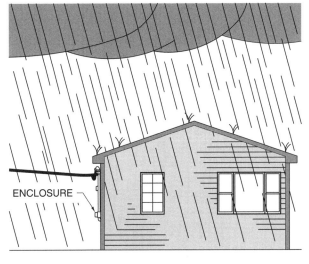

_____ **5.** Required enclosure is NEMA ___.

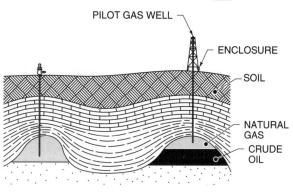
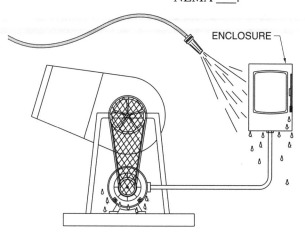

PILOT GAS WELL

ENCLOSURE

SOIL

NATURAL GAS

CRUDE OIL

_____ **6.** Required enclosure is NEMA ___.

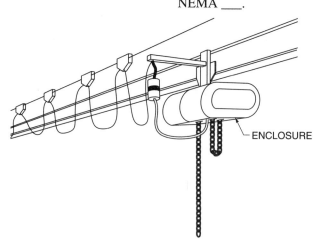

ENCLOSURE

_____ **7.** Required enclosure is NEMA ___.

ENCLOSURE

_____ **8.** Required enclosure is NEMA ___.

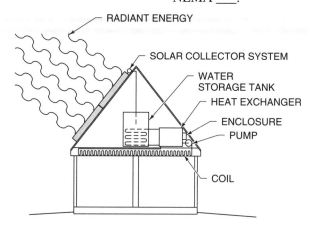

RADIANT ENERGY

SOLAR COLLECTOR SYSTEM

WATER STORAGE TANK

HEAT EXCHANGER

ENCLOSURE

PUMP

COIL

_____ **9.** Required enclosure is NEMA ___.

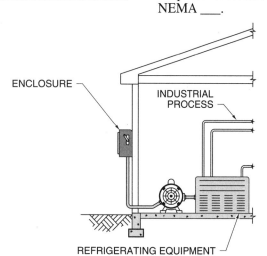

ENCLOSURE

INDUSTRIAL PROCESS

REFRIGERATING EQUIPMENT

_____ **10.** Required enclosure is NEMA ___.

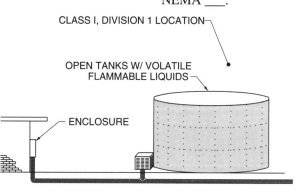

CLASS I, DIVISION 1 LOCATION

OPEN TANKS W/ VOLATILE FLAMMABLE LIQUIDS

ENCLOSURE

Contactors and Motor Starters

Worksheet 8-2

Name _____ Date _____

Wire Reference Numbers

Use Data Sheet A on page 250 to assign a wire number to each wire in the line diagrams. Write each number directly above the wire.

1. The circuit is designed so that two magnetic motor starters are operated by two start/stop pushbutton stations with a common emergency stop. Assign the proper wire numbers to the wires of the two pilot lights so that, when connected to the circuit, the red pilot light glows when magnetic motor starter M1 is ON and the green pilot light glows when magnetic motor starter M2 is ON.

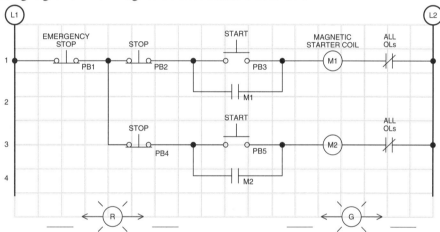

2. The circuit is designed with pushbuttons arranged for a sequence control of two motor starters. Assign the proper wire numbers to the wires of the foot switch and pushbutton so that, when connected to the circuit, the foot switch starts coil M1 and the pushbutton starts coil M2.

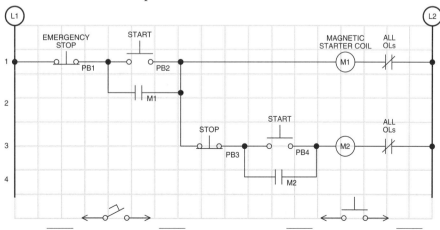

Contactors and Motor Starters

Worksheet 8-3

Name _____   Date _____

Basic Motor Control

Complete the wiring diagram according to the line diagram. Do not make any wire splices or additional terminal connections on the wiring diagram. All connections should run from terminal screw to terminal screw.

1. Draw the wiring diagram of the start/stop pushbutton station with memory.

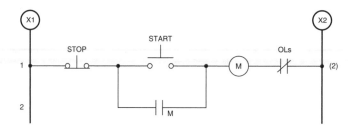

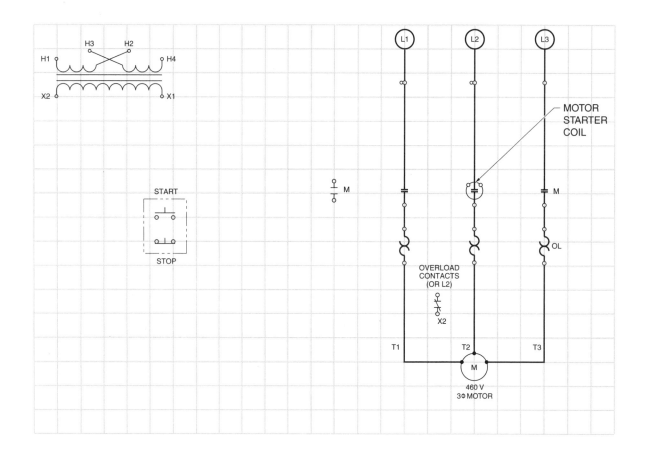

Contactors and Motor Starters

Worksheet 8-4

Name _____   Date _____

Motor Control with Pilot Light

Complete the wiring diagram according to the line diagram. Do not make any wire splices or additional terminal connections on the wiring diagram. All connections should run from terminal screw to terminal screw.

1. Draw the wiring diagram of the start/stop pushbutton station with memory and a pilot light that turns ON when the motor is not running. There is overload protection for the motor.

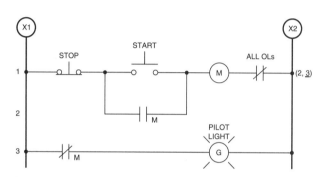

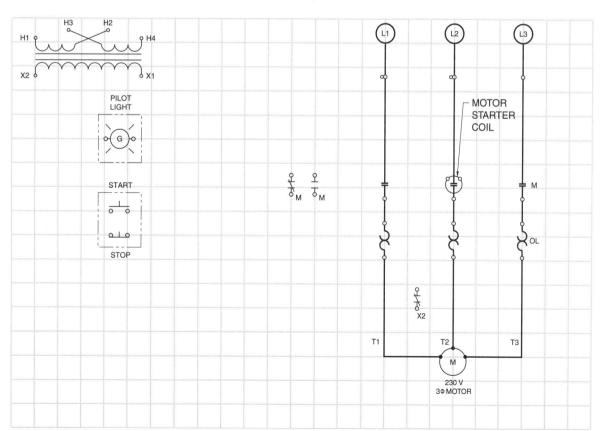

Contactors and Motor Starters

Name _____   Date _____

Multiple Control Stations

Complete the wiring diagram according to the line diagram. Do not make any wire splices or additional terminal connections on the wiring diagram. All connections should run from terminal screw to terminal screw.

1. Draw the wiring diagram of the three start/stop pushbutton stations with memory that control a single motor starter. There is overload protection for the motor.

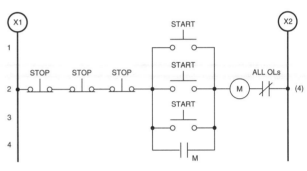

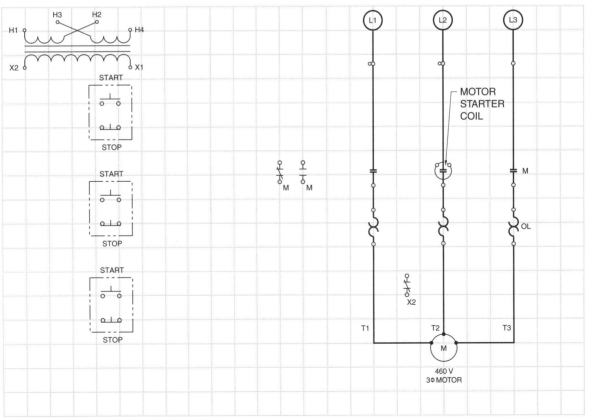

Contactors and Motor Starters

Worksheet 8-6

Name _____ Date _____

Multiple Motor Control

Complete the wiring diagram according to the line diagram. Do not make any wire splices or additional terminal connections on the wiring diagram. All connections should run from terminal screw to terminal screw.

1. Draw the wiring diagram of the start/stop pushbutton station with memory that controls two motor starters. The motor starters are wired so that if a maintained overload occurs on either one, both are automatically disconnected from the line. This is accomplished by wiring the holding circuit of each motor starter through the auxiliary contacts of the other. The circuit also provides for a sequence start of each motor to avoid the problems that could arise from both motors starting simultaneously.

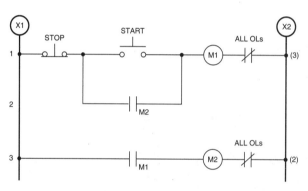

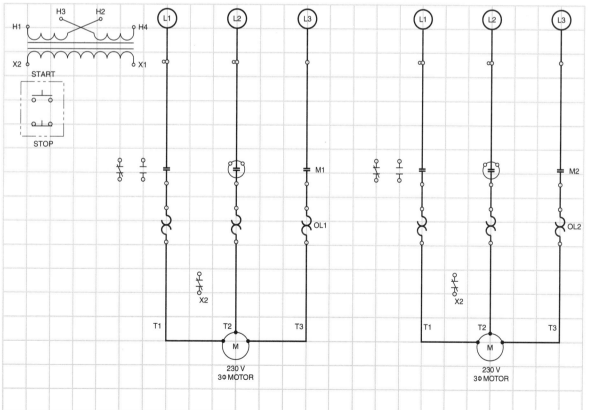

Contactors and Motor Starters

Worksheet 8-7

Name _____   Date _____

Multiple Control of Multiple Motors

Complete the wiring diagram according to the line diagram. Do not make any wire splices or additional terminal connections on the wiring diagram. All connections should run from terminal screw to terminal screw.

1. Draw the wiring diagram of the two separate start/stop pushbutton stations with memory that control two separate motor starters. A master stop pushbutton is included to turn OFF both motor starters. The overload relays on both motor starters are wired in series so that both drop out when a maintained overload occurs in either one.

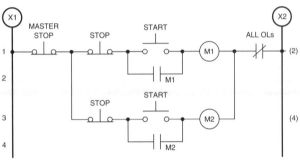

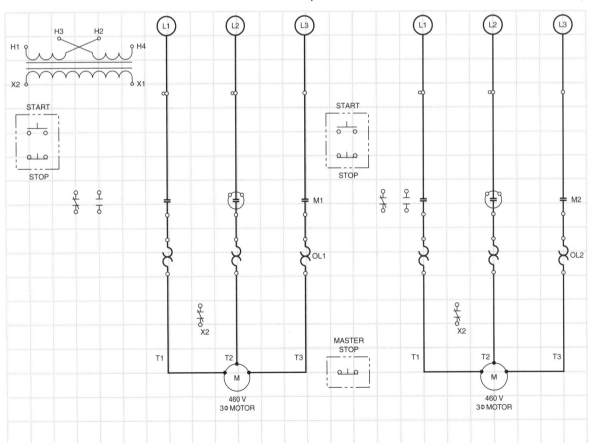

Contactors and Motor Starters

Worksheet 8-8

Name _____ Date _____

Circuit Wiring

Use Data Sheet B on page 254 to wire the equipment. All wire splices should be inside the enclosures and conduit. Do not make any wire splices that are not necessary.

1. Wire the equipment as required by the conduit and enclosure arrangement. Power feed is through the start/ stop enclosure.

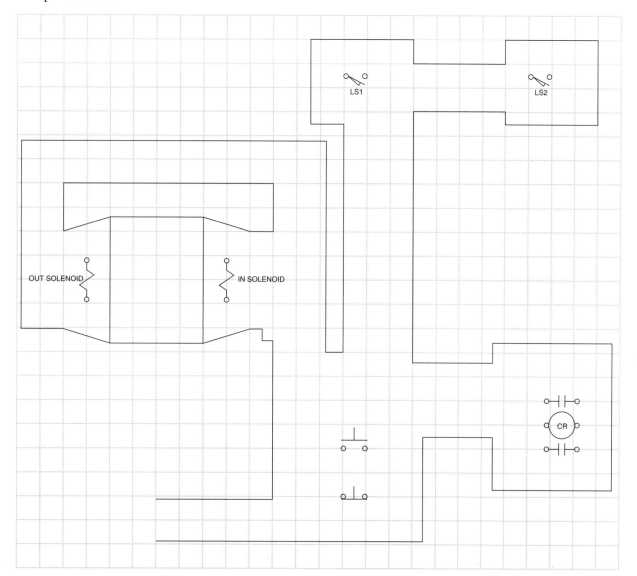

2. Wire the equipment as required by the conduit and enclosure arrangement. Power feed is through the limit switch enclosure.

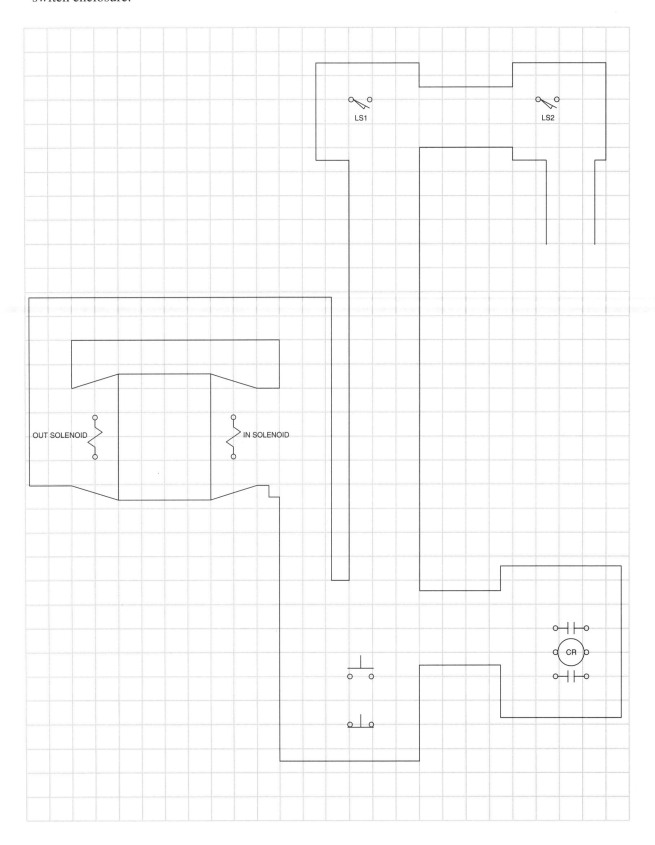

3. Wire the equipment as required by the conduit and enclosure arrangement. Power feed is through the control relay enclosure.

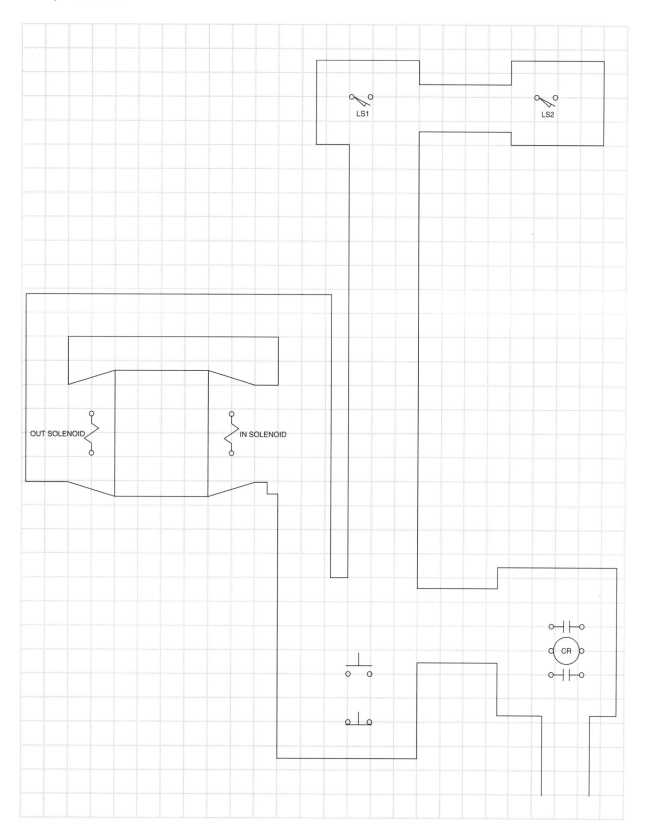

4. Wire the equipment as required by the conduit and enclosure arrangement. Power feed is through the solenoid valve.

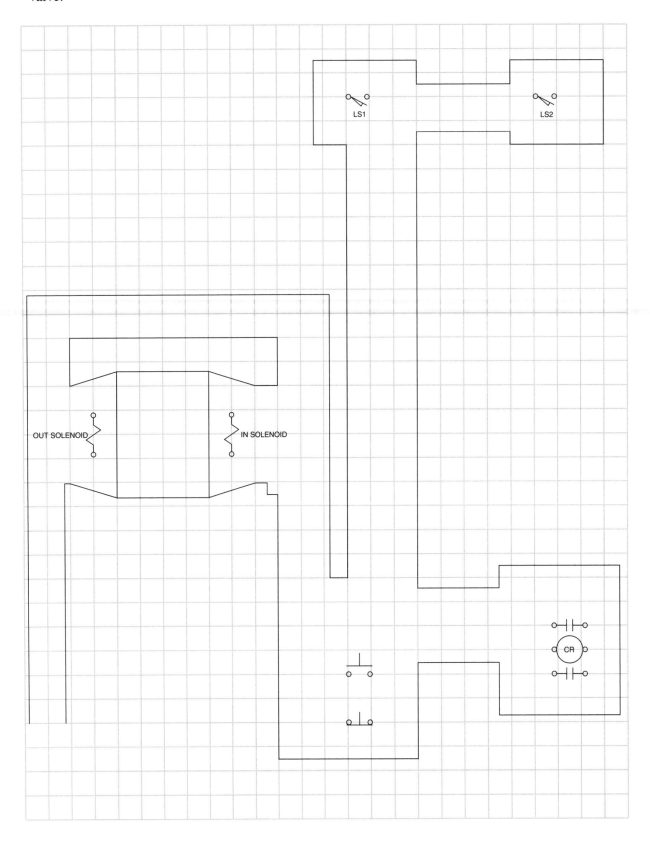

Control Devices

Tech-Chek 9

Name _____ Date _____

Electrical Motor Controls

_____ 1. A(n) ___ is the device that is pressed, pulled, or rotated by an individual.

_____ 2. A(n) ___ is the part of a limit switch that transfers the mechanical fork of the moving part to the electrical contacts.

_____ 3. ___ is the amount of pressure that must be removed before the switch contacts reset for another cycle after the setpoint has been reached and the switch activated.

_____ 4. A(n) ___ is a mechanical input that requires physical contact of the object with the switch actuator.

_____ 5. A(n) ___ actuator is an actuator that has a long arm that may be cut to the required length.

_____ 6. A ___ pressure-sensing device is rated for 10,000 psi or more.
A. bellows   C. piston
B. diaphragm   D. spring

_____ 7. A ___ level switch is used to detect product dielectric variations.
A. mechanical   C. conductive probe
B. magnetic   D. capacitive

_____ 8. ___ loads are the least destructive loads to switch.

_____ 9. Most flow switches are designed to operate in the ___ position.
A. horizontal   C. curved
B. vertical   D. circular

_____ 10. A(n) ___ is used to control the yawing function of a windmill.
A. anemometer   C. pressure switch
B. wind vane   D. flow switch

_____ 11. A(n) ___ button operator allows for easy emergency stops and valve shutoffs.
A. jumbo mushroom   C. half-shrouded
B. extended   D. flush

_____ 12. A(n) ___ is a temperature-sensitive resistor that changes its electrical resistance with a change in temperature.

_____ 13. A(n) ___ is an output used to switch high-power DC loads.
A. transistor   C. SCR
B. triac   D. PTC

_____ **14.** A(n) ___ is an output used to switch low-power DC loads.
      A. transistor   C. SCR
      B. triac   D. PTC

_____ **15.** Charging and discharging tank applications are also known as pump and ___ control.

_____ **16.** A(n) ___ is a switch used in fire protection systems to detect burning material.

_____ **17.** The ___ contacts of a pressure switch are used when the pressure switch is used to maintain system pressure.

_____ **18.** A(n) ___ switch is used to maintain a predetermined pressure in a tank or reservoir.

_____ **19.** A(n) ___ device is a device that includes an electronic circuit that provides communication and diagnostic capabilities to the device.

_____ **20.** In a(n) ___ circuit, inputs such as limit switches and temperature switches are wired into the system and at least one set of wires must go to each input device.

Joystick Truth Table

Complete the truth table for the joystick circuit. Place an X in the appropriate box to indicate the closed contacts.

1.

POSITION	CONTACTS			
	A	B	C	D
RIGHT				
LEFT				
UP				
DOWN				

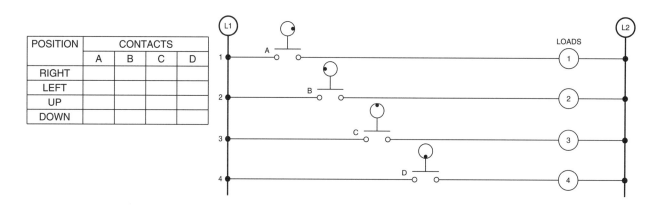

Limit Switch Connections

Determine whether the limit switches are correctly or incorrectly installed.

_____ **1.** Limit Switch 1 is ___ installed.

_____ **2.** Limit Switch 2 is ___ installed.

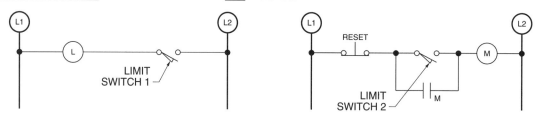

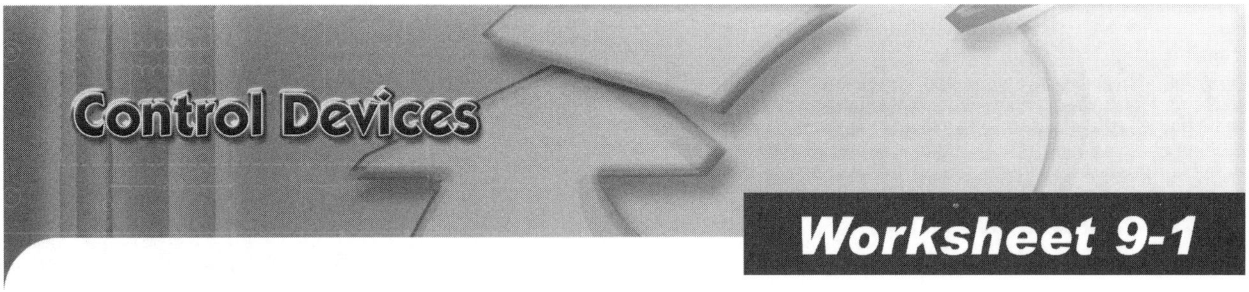

Control Devices

Name _____   Date _____

Circuit Truth Tables

Complete the truth tables for the circuits. Place an X in the appropriate box to indicate the closed contacts.

1.

POSITION	CONTACTS			
	A	B	C	D
AUTO				
HAND				

2.

POSITION	CONTACTS			
	A	B	C	D
UP				
DOWN				
RIGHT				

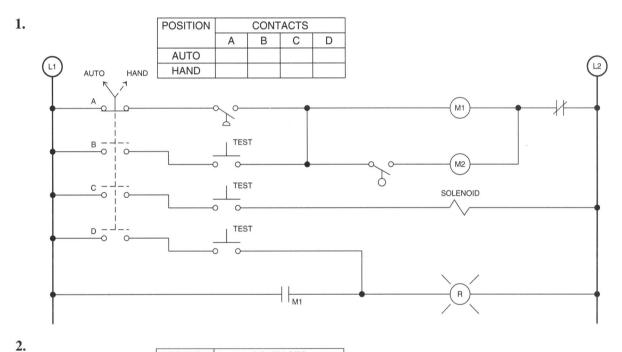

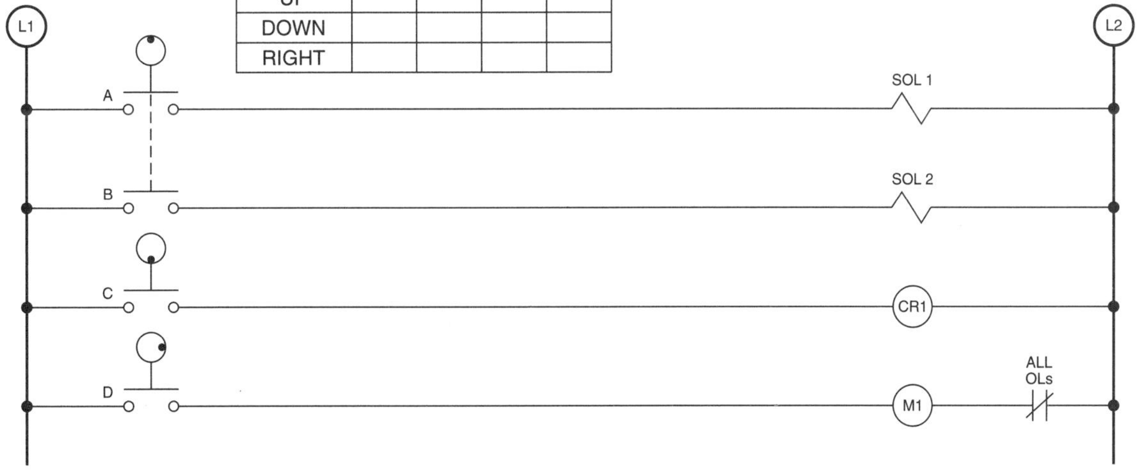

Control Devices

Worksheet 9-2

Name _____ Date _____

Heating Element Control

Complete the line and wiring diagrams according to the circuit information. Use standard lettering, numbering, and coding information.

1. Design a circuit in which a temperature switch is used to control a load even though the temperature switch contacts cannot directly handle the load. The heating contactor should energize at a low temperature setting.

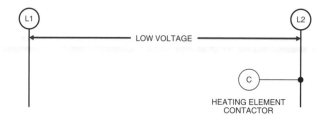

2. Complete the power circuit wiring diagram as a 3φ wye-connected set of heating elements.

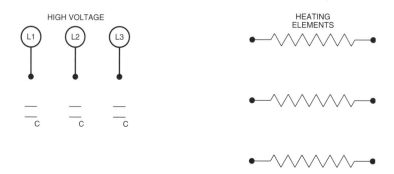

3. Complete the power circuit wiring diagram as a 3φ delta-connected set of heating elements.

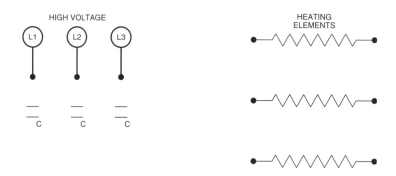

Control Devices

Worksheet 9-3

Name _____ Date _____

Vacuum Sensing

Complete the line diagrams according to the circuit information. Use standard lettering, numbering, and coding information.

1. Design a circuit with a vacuum switch that sounds a warning bell if a loss of vacuum occurs.

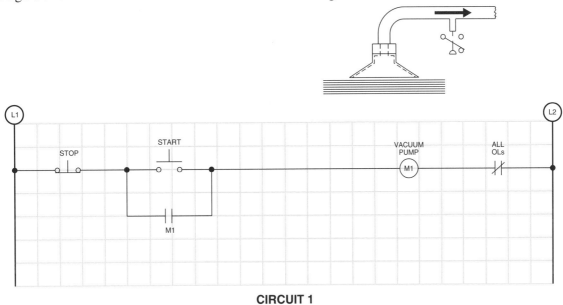

CIRCUIT 1

2. Redraw Circuit 1, adding a timer so the vacuum switch does not activate the bell unless the loss of vacuum occurs after the pump has run for 60 sec.

Control Devices

Worksheet 9-4

Name _____ Date _____

Pressure Control

Complete the line diagram based on the circuit information. Use standard lettering, numbering, and coding information.

1. Design a circuit with three pressure switches to maintain the proper amount of air pressure in an inflatable building. One pressure switch controls an air pump to keep the building inflated. A second switch detects overpressure that could rupture the building and warns of overpressure by sounding a bell. The third switch detects underpressure that could cause the building to collapse and warns of underpressure by sounding a horn.

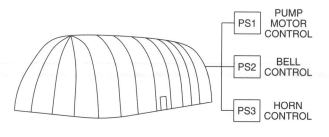

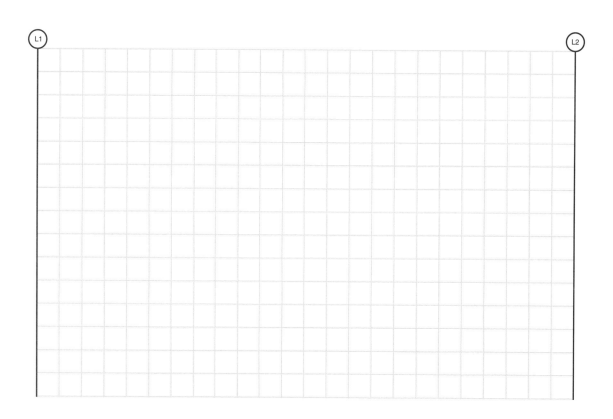

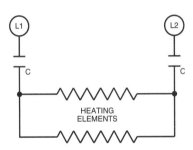

Control Devices

Worksheet 9-5

Name _____ Date _____

Dual-Temperature Control

Complete the line diagram based on the circuit information. Use standard lettering, numbering, and coding information.

1. Design a circuit with two separate temperature switches and a selector switch to provide two temperature controls. Heat is provided by heating elements activated through a magnetic contactor. The selector switch has three settings: high, low, and OFF. Temperature Switch 1 controls the high temperature and Temperature Switch 2 controls the low temperature. Complete the truth table for the selector switch to illustrate the circuit operation.

POSITION	CONTACTS	
	A	B
HIGH		
OFF		
LOW		

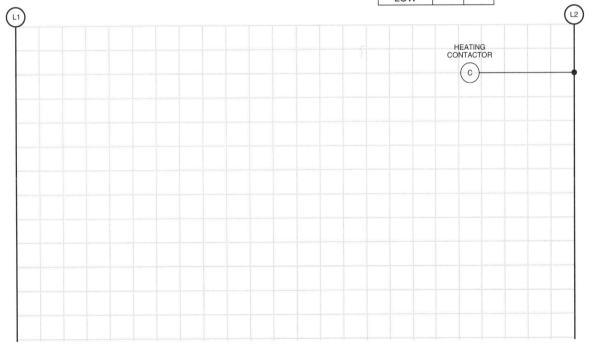

Control Devices

Worksheet 9-6

Name _____ Date _____

Fan/Heater Control

Complete the line diagram based on the circuit information. Use standard lettering, numbering, and coding information.

1. Design a circuit with a standard start/stop pushbutton station to control a fan motor and an electric heating contactor. Add a flow switch to ensure that the proper amount of air flow is present when the fan motor and heater are ON. A bell sounds if the flow is restricted when the fan is ON, but does not sound if the fan motor is OFF.

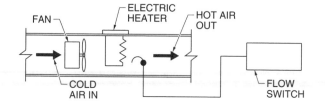

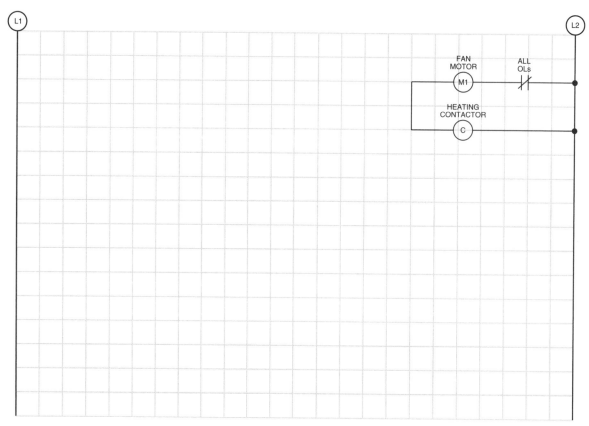

CIRCUIT 1

2. Redraw Circuit 1, adding a timer to keep the ventilation fan motor from operating for 30 sec after the heating element is turned ON. This allows a 30 sec warm-up period.

3. Redraw Circuit 1, changing the control from a pushbutton control circuit to an automatic temperature control circuit. Include a two-position selector switch that can be placed in an automatic position or an OFF position. In the automatic position, the temperature switch maintains the correct temperature. In the OFF position, the heating element and fan motor cannot operate.

Control Devices

Worksheet 9-7

Name _____ Date _____

Level Control Relay

Use Data Sheet C on page 255 to complete the line diagram. Use standard lettering, numbering, and coding information.

1. Design a circuit where the relay is connected to control a pump motor. The relay is connected to monitor two levels of fluid. The pump motor turns ON when the maximum level setting is reached, and stays ON until the minimum level setting is reached. Indicate only those connections necessary to form the control circuit.

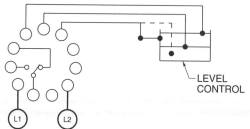

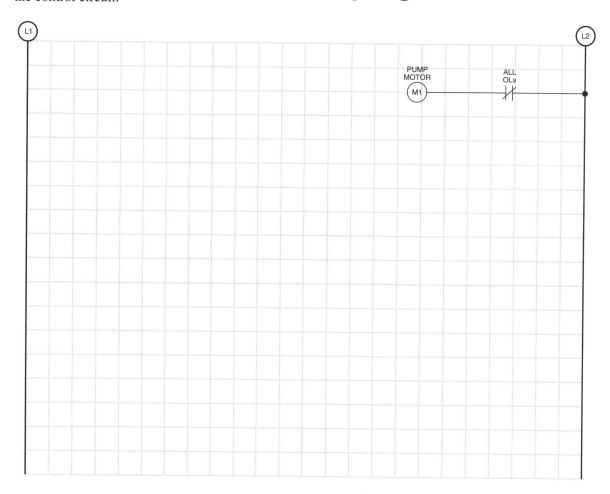

Reversing Motor Circuits

Tech-Chek 10

Name _____ Date _____

Electrical Motor Controls

_____ 1. The industry standard is to interchange power leads L1 and ___ to reverse the direction of rotation of a 3φ motor.

_____ 2. A(n) ___ is the arrangement of contacts in such a way that both sets cannot be closed at the same time.

_____ 3. It is necessary to interchange only the ___ winding to reverse the direction of rotation of a 1φ motor.

_____ 4. The ___ winding of a 1φ motor normally has a much lower resistance than the ___ winding.

_____ 5. A manual starter can be used to reverse the direction of current flow through the ___ of all DC motors.

_____ 6. A(n) ___ is a manual switch made up of moving contacts mounted on an insulated rotating shaft.

_____ 7. ___ wiring is wiring in which each component in a circuit is connected to the next component.

_____ 8. When troubleshooting a reversing circuit, the voltage must be within ___% of the control circuit rating.

_____ 9. A(n) ___ circuit allows the operator to start the motor for a short time without memory.

_____ 10. A drum switch is not considered a motor starter because the switch does not contain ___.

_____ 11. Although most magnetic reversing starters provide mechanical interlock protection, some circuits are provided with a secondary backup system that uses ___ contacts to provide electrical interlocking.

_____ 12. In a(n) ___ reversing circuit, interlocking is accomplished by programming, not hard wiring, normally closed auxiliary contacts into the circuit.

_____ 13. In a(n) ___ reversing circuit, memory is accomplished by programming, not hard wiring, normally open auxiliary contacts into the circuit.

_____ 14. The stop, forward, and reverse pushbuttons are wired to the ___ section of a PLC.

_____ 15. The forward and reverse starting coils are wired to the ___ section of a PLC.

_____ **16.** The industrial standard of reversing the direction of rotation of a DC motor is to reverse the direction of current through the ___.

_____ **17.** ___ switches can be incorporated to shut an operation down if a load travels far enough to be unsafe.

T   F   **18.** A direct hard wired circuit is easy to modify.

_____ **19.** When wiring using a(n) ___, each wire in the control circuit is assigned a reference point on the line diagram to identify the different wires that connect the components in the circuit.
            A. PLC   C. limit switch
            B. terminal strip   D. electric motor drive

_____ **20.** ___ eliminate the need for forward and reversing starters because they can be used to select motor direction.

T   F   **21.** When using a PLC, an input can be wired normally open and programmed either normally open or normally closed.

T   F   **22.** Two manual starters are connected together to create a manual reversing starter.

_____ **23.** A(n) ___ can monitor and control all motor control functions, but cannot directly monitor and display motor parameters such as voltage, current, frequency, and power.

_____ **24.** A drum switch may be purchased with maintained contacts or ___ contacts.

_____ **25.** ___ interlocking may be used in either or both mechanical or auxiliary interlocking.

_____ **26.** Although the power circuit and control circuit operate together to control a motor, they are electrically isolated from each other through a ___.

Reversing Motor Circuits

Worksheet 10-1

Name _____   Date _____

Reversing 1ϕ Motors

Use Data Sheet D on page 256 to draw the wiring diagram. Note: *Use only the number of contacts required.*

1. Operate the motor in forward and reverse at 115 VAC.

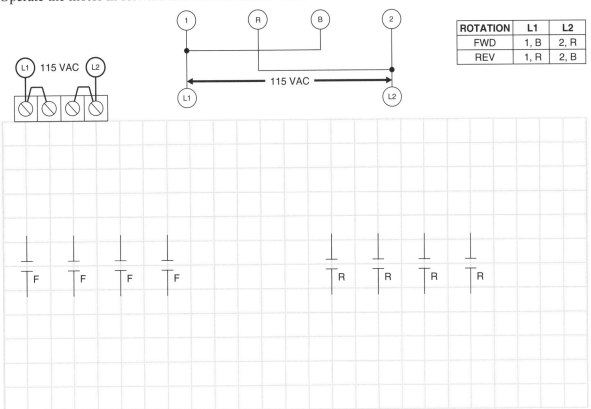

ROTATION	L1	L2
FWD	1, B	2, R
REV	1, R	2, B

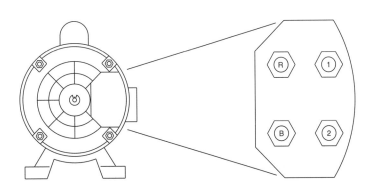

Reversing Motor Circuits

Worksheet 10-2

Name _____ Date _____

Reversing 3φ Motors

Use Data Sheet D on page 256 to draw the wiring diagram. Note: *Interchange any two power leads to reverse the rotation of the motor. The accepted standard is to interchange leads T1 and T3. Use only the number of contacts required.*

1. Operate the motor in forward and reverse at 230 VAC.

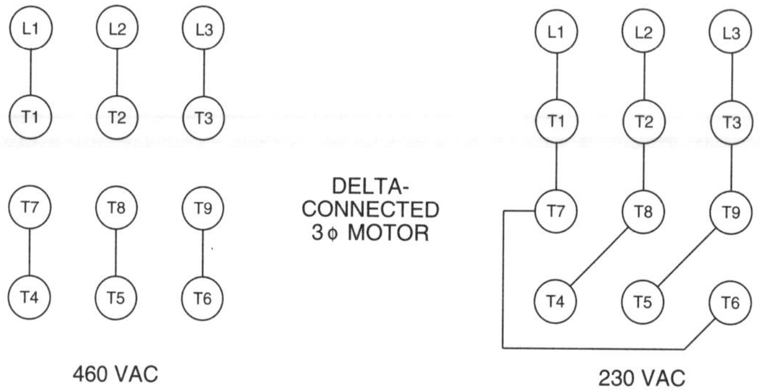

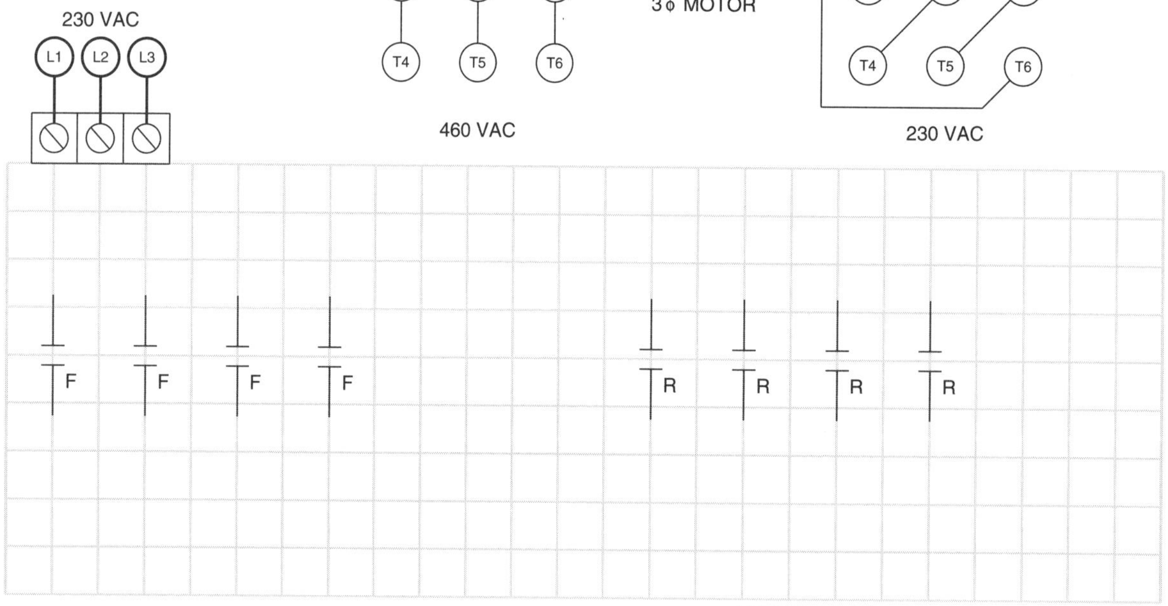

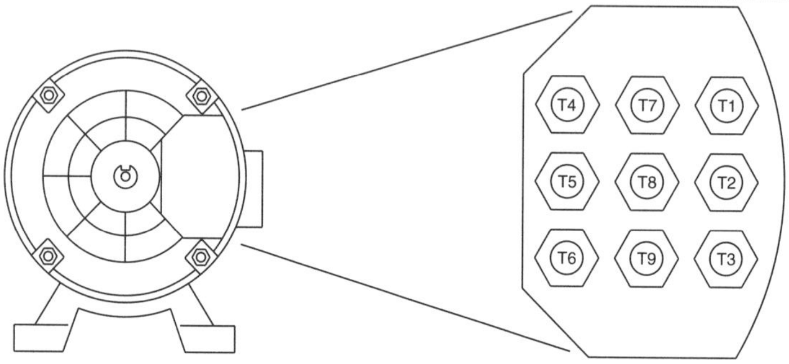

DELTA-CONNECTED 3φ MOTOR

460 VAC

230 VAC

230 VAC

Reversing Motor Circuits

Worksheet 10-3

Name _____   Date _____

Reversing Dual-Voltage, 1φ Motors at Low Voltage

Use Data Sheet D on page 256 to draw the wiring diagram. Note: Interchange the red and black leads to reverse the motor rotation. Use only the number of contacts required.

1. Operate the motor in forward and reverse at 120 VAC.

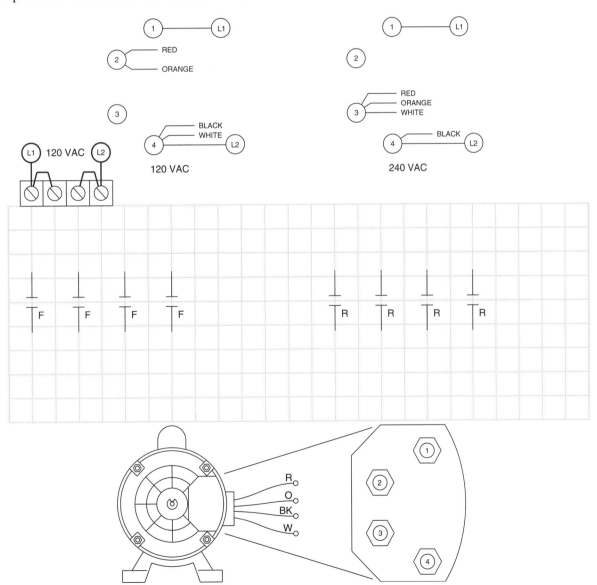

Reversing Motor Circuits

Name _____ Date _____

Reversing Dual-Voltage, 1ϕ Motors at High Voltage

Use Data Sheet D on page 256 to draw the wiring diagram. Note: *Interchange the red and black leads to reverse the motor rotation. Use only the number of contacts required.*

1. Operate the motor in forward and reverse at 230 VAC.

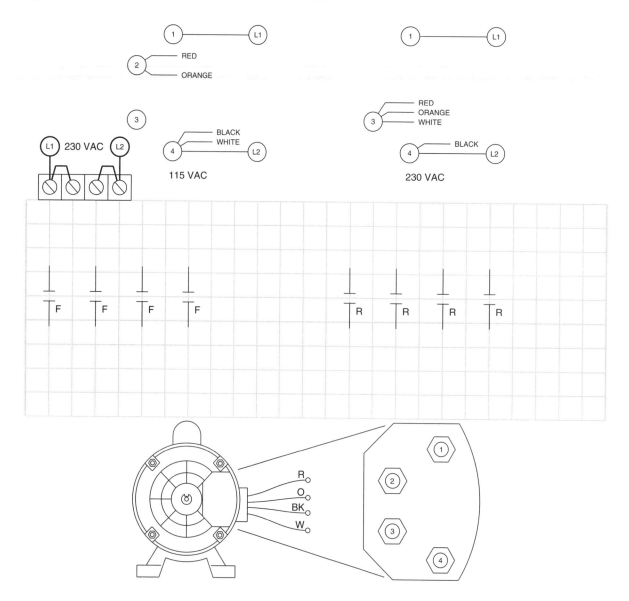

Reversing Motor Circuits

Worksheet 10-5

Name _____   Date _____

Reversing 1ϕ Motors – All Wires Not Used

Use Data Sheet D on page 256 to draw the wiring diagram. Note: Interchange the red and black leads to reverse the motor rotation. Use only the number of contacts required.

1. Operate the motor in forward and reverse at 230 VAC.

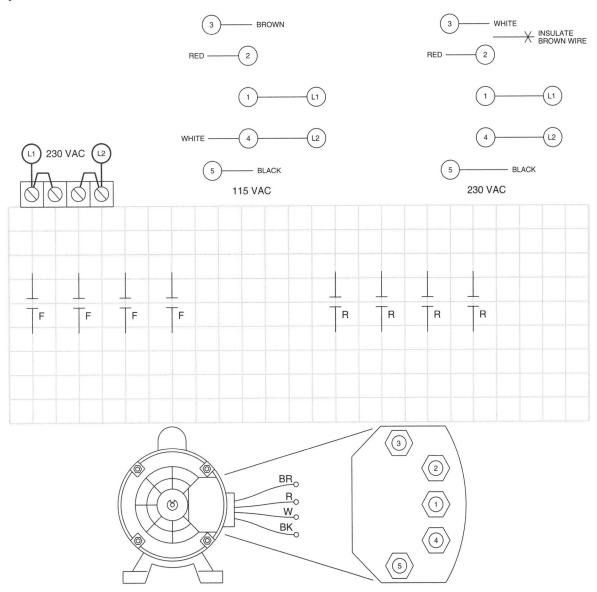

Reversing Motor Circuits

Name _____ Date _____

Interchanging Motor Leads

Use Data Sheet D on page 256 to draw the wiring diagram. Note: *Interchange the red and black leads to reverse the motor rotation. Use only the number of contacts required.*

1. Operate the motor in forward and reverse at 115 VAC.

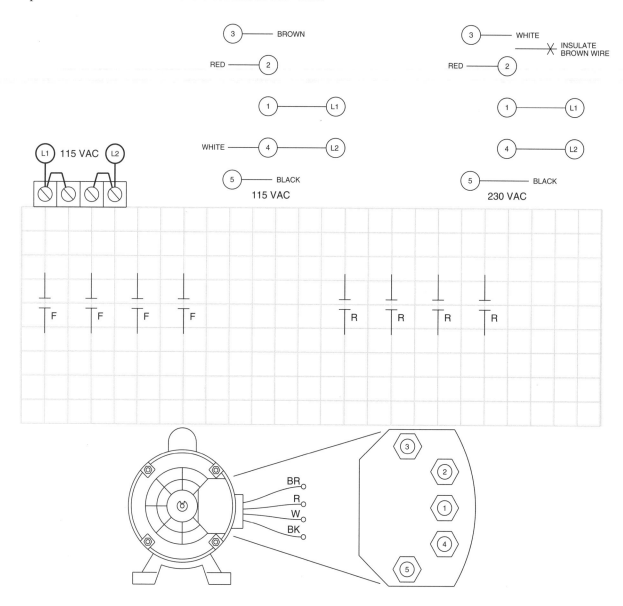

Reversing Motor Circuits

Name _____   Date _____

Reversing Two-Speed, 1ϕ Motors at Low Speed

Use Data Sheet D on page 256 to draw the wiring diagram. Note: Interchange the red and black leads to reverse the motor rotation. Use only the number of contacts required.

1. Operate the motor in forward and reverse at low speed.

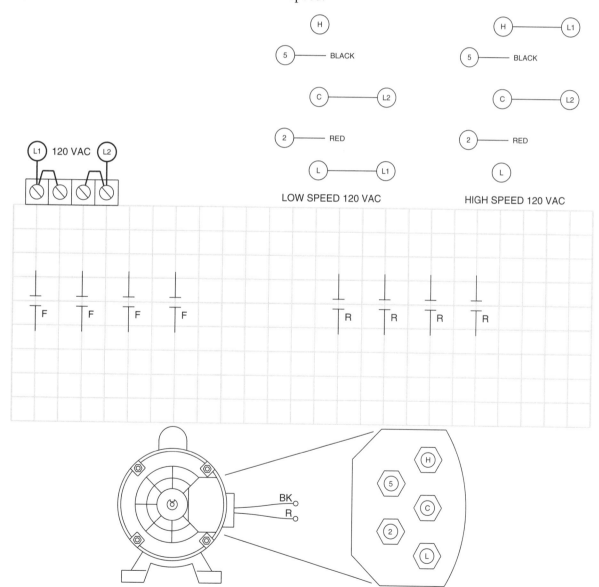

Reversing Motor Circuits

Name _____   Date _____

Reversing Two-Speed, 1φ Motors at High Speed

Use Data Sheet D on page 256 to draw the wiring diagram. Note: *Interchange the red and black leads to reverse the motor rotation. Use only the number of contacts required.*

1. Operate the motor in forward and reverse at high speed.

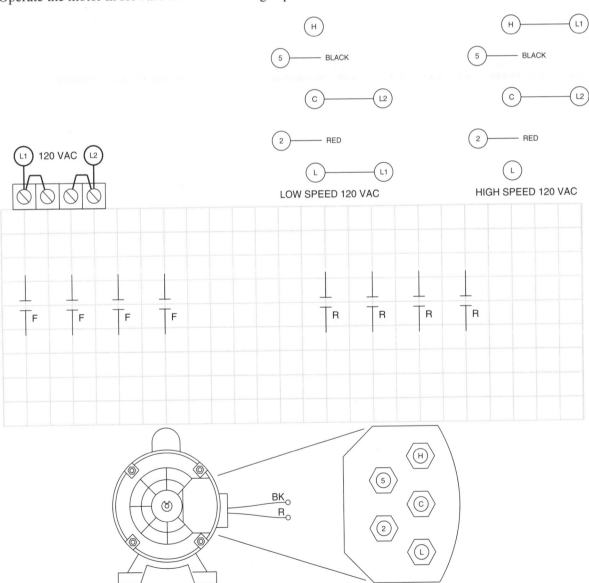

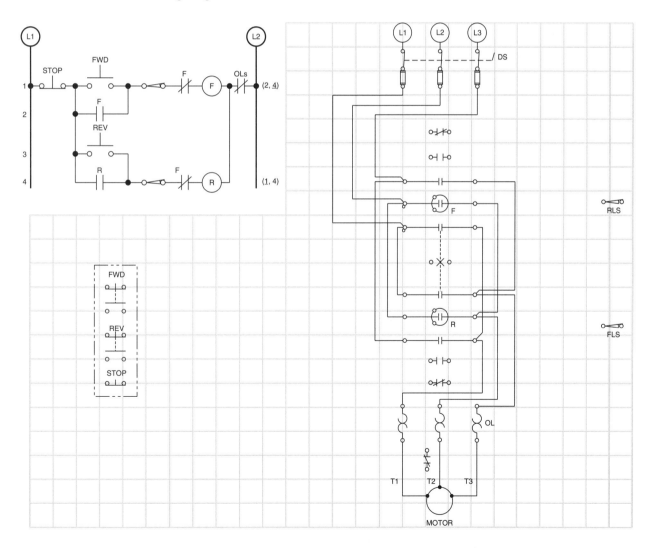

Reversing Motor Circuits

Name _____   Date _____

Limit Switch Motor Stopping

The line diagram is of a standard forward/reverse/stop pushbutton station for forwarding and reversing a motor. Included in the circuit are mechanical and auxiliary contact interlocking. Also included are a forward limit switch to stop the motor in forward and a reverse limit switch to stop the motor in reverse. Overload protection is common to both forward and reverse directions.

1. Complete the wiring diagram based on the line diagram. Do not make any wire splices or additional terminal connections on the wiring diagram. All connections must run from terminal screw to terminal screw.

Reversing Motor Circuits

Worksheet 10-10

Name _____ Date _____

Forward/Reverse Circuit with Indicator Lights

The line diagram is of a standard forward/reverse/stop pushbutton station with indicating lights to show the direction of motor rotation. The indicating lights are to be mounted within the pushbutton enclosure. Overload protection is common to both forward and reverse directions.

1. Complete the wiring diagram based on the line diagram. Do not make any wire splices or additional terminal connections on the wiring diagram. All connections must run from terminal screw to terminal screw.

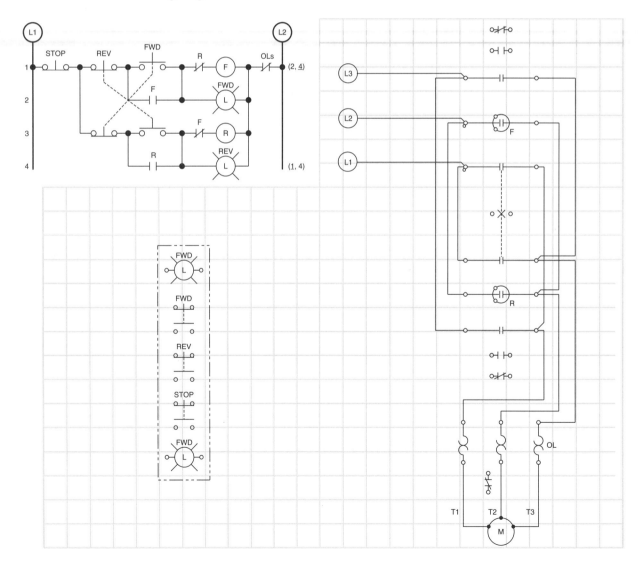

Reversing Motor Circuits

Worksheet 10-11

Name _____ Date _____

Selector Switch Motor Control

The line diagram is of a standard start/stop pushbutton station with a selector switch to control direction of motor travel. A visual indication of the direction of motor rotation is provided on the selector switch in case the motor and drive unit cannot be seen from the control station. Overload protection is common to forward and reverse directions.

1. Complete the wiring diagram based on the line diagram. Do not make any wire splices or additional terminal connections on the wiring diagram. All connections must run from terminal screw to terminal screw.

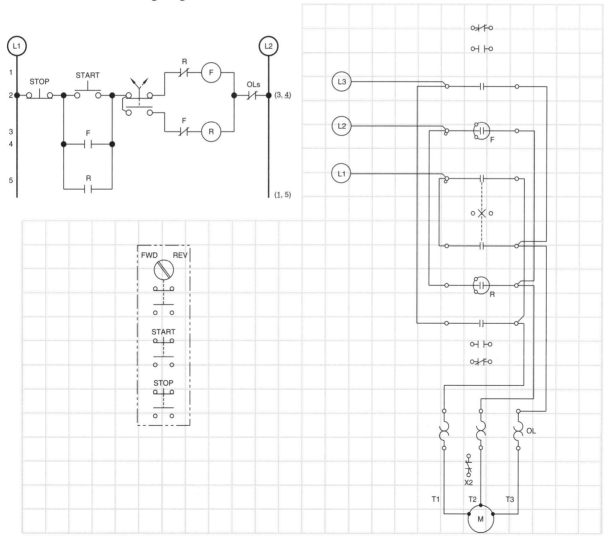

Reversing Motor Circuits

Worksheet 10-12

Name _____ Date _____

Selector Switch Jog/Run Control

The line diagram is of a standard forward/reverse/stop pushbutton station with a selector switch to provide for jogging or running. The forward and reverse pushbuttons energize the motor only as long as they are pressed when the selector switch is in the jog position. The forward and reverse pushbuttons operate as a standard pushbutton station with memory when the selector switch is in the run position. Overload protection is common to both forward and reverse directions.

1. Complete the wiring diagram based on the line diagram. Do not make any wire splices or additional terminal connections on the wiring diagram. All connections must run from terminal screw to terminal screw.

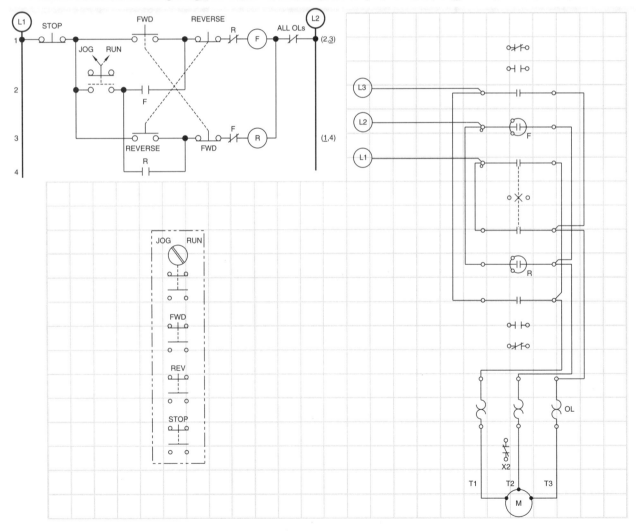

Reversing Motor Circuits

Worksheet 10-13

Name _____ Date _____

Reversing AC Motors

A manual reversing starter is a switch that includes overload protection. Overload protection protects the motor when running and automatically disconnects an overloaded motor. To prevent a short circuit and damage to the motor, the starter provides mechanical interlocking. Mechanical interlocking prevents the forward and reverse contacts from being energized at the same time. Manual reversing starters are normally used with motors less than 2 HP.

State the connections for a 3ϕ motor and motor starter.

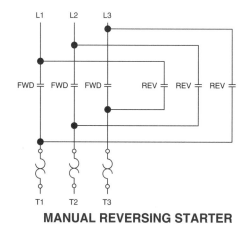

MANUAL REVERSING STARTER

Forward

_____ **1.** ____ to T1

_____ **2.** ____ to T2

_____ **3.** ____ to T3

Reverse

_____ **4.** ____ to T1

_____ **5.** ____ to T2

_____ **6.** ____ to T3

State the connections for a 1ϕ (split-phase) motor and motor starter.

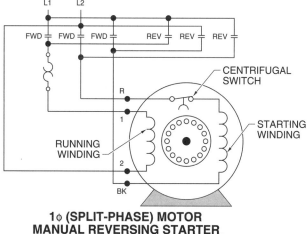

**1ϕ (SPLIT-PHASE) MOTOR
MANUAL REVERSING STARTER**

Forward

_____ **7.** ____ to 1

_____ **8.** ____ to red

_____ **9.** ____ to black

Reverse

_____ **10.** ____ to 1

_____ **11.** ____ to red

_____ **12.** ____ to black

Reversing DC Motors

The rotation of a DC series, shunt, or compound motor depends on the direction of the current flow in the field circuit and the armature circuit. To reverse the rotation, the current direction in the field or the armature is reversed. Normally, the current through the armature is reversed. Standard abbreviations are used with DC motors: A1, A2 = armature; F1, F2 = shunt field; S1, S2 = series field.

State the connections for a DC shunt motor and a motor starter.

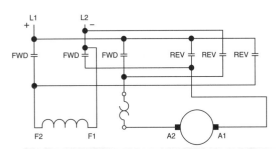

DC SHUNT MOTOR REVERSING STARTER

Forward

_____ **13.** ____ to A1

_____ **14.** ____ to A2

_____ **15.** ____ to F1

Reverse

_____ **16.** ____ to A1

_____ **17.** ____ to A2

_____ **18.** ____ to F1

State the connections for a DC series compound motor and motor starter.

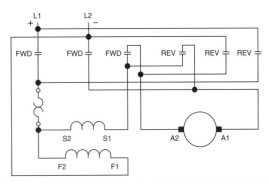

DC COMPOUND MOTOR REVERSING STARTER

Forward

_____ **19.** ____ to S2/F2

_____ **20.** ____ to S1

_____ **21.** ____ to L2/F1

Reverse

_____ **22.** ____ to S2/F2

_____ **23.** ____ to S1

_____ **24.** ____ to L2/F1

Reversing Motor Circuits

Worksheet 10-14

Name _____ Date _____

Motor Control Circuits

1. Draw a line diagram of the motor control circuit.

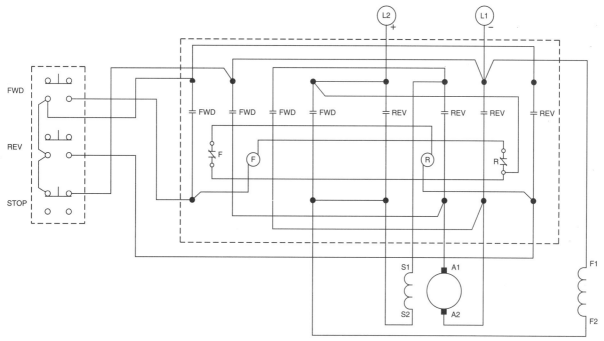

MOTOR CONTROL CIRCUIT

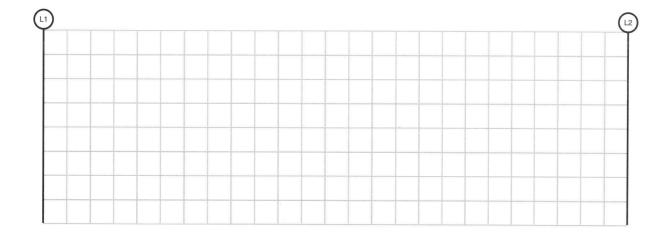

Answer the questions using the motor control circuit on page 115.

_____ 2. If the motor is not running, can the motor be started in either the forward or reverse direction?

_____ 3. If the motor is running in the forward direction, will pressing the reverse pushbutton energize the reverse starter coil?

_____ 4. If the motor is running in the reverse direction, will pressing the forward pushbutton change the direction of motor rotation?

_____ 5. Does the motor starter provide overload protection?

_____ 6. Does the stop pushbutton have to be pressed to change the direction of rotation when the motor is running?

_____ 7. A(n) ___ DC motor is changing direction.

Power Distribution Systems

Tech-Chek 11

Name _____ Date _____

Electrical Motor Controls

_____ **1.** A(n) ___ is an overcurrent protection device with a link that melts and opens the circuit on an overcurrent condition.

_____ **2.** A(n) ___ connection is made when the three ends of separate phases are connected together, creating a common wire.

_____ **3.** A(n) ___ connection is made when the end of one separate phase is connected to the beginning of the next phase, etc.

_____ **4.** A(n) ___ is a metal-enclosed distribution system of ___ available in prefabricated sections.

_____ **5.** A(n) ___ diagram uses single lines and symbols to show system components and operation.

_____ **6.** All transformer installations must follow ___ and ___ requirements.

_____ **7.** In a transformer, a marking of X1 or X2 indicates the ___ voltage side.
    A. high   C. primary
    B. low   D. neither A, B, nor C

_____ **8.** The voltage regulator on a transformer is provided with ___ to allow for a variable output.

_____ **9.** NEC® Section 450.21 (B) states that all dry-type transformers over 112½ kVA rating shall be installed in a(n) ___ room.

_____ **10.** Switchboards are designed for use as ___, distribution, or a combination of both.

_____ **11.** Panelboards contain overcurrent protection devices for lighting, appliance, and ___ circuits.

_____ **12.** A(n) ___ is a reusable OCPD that opens a circuit automatically at a predetermined overcurrent.

_____ **13.** The two basic types of busways are feeder and ___ busways.

_____ **14.** ___ is the process of delivering electrical power where it is needed.

_____ **15.** Switchboards that have more than ___ switches or circuit breakers must include a main switch to protect or disconnect all circuits.

_____ **16.** When taking measurements inside an enclosure, the enclosure should be tested to make sure it is ___.

_____ **17.** To meter the incoming power, a switchboard must have a(n) ___ to measure power usage.

_____ **18.** The capacity of transformers is rated in ___.

_____ **19.** The three main sections of a substation are the primary switchgear, transformer, and ___ sections.

_____ **20.** Switchboards are rated by the manufacturer for maximum voltage and ___ output.

_____ **21.** A(n) ___ circuit is the portion of a distribution system between the final overcurrent protection device and the outlet or load connected to it.

_____ **22.** A(n) ___ electrode is a conductor embedded in the earth to provide a good ground.

_____ **23.** ___ perform the same function as fuses and are tested the same way.

_____ **24.** NEC® Article 408.15 states that not more than ___ overcurrent devices for a lighting and appliance panelboard, other than mains, are permitted in one cabinet.

_____ **25.** The function of a substation includes ___.
A. receiving voltage and increasing it to an appropriate level
B. providing a safe point for disconnecting power
C. providing a place to adjust and regulate outgoing voltage
D. all of the above

_____ **26.** A(n) ___ is the piece of equipment which a large block of electric power is delivered to from a substation and broken down into smaller blocks for distribution throughout a building.

_____ **27.** A(n) ___ is a wall-mounted distribution cabinet containing a group of overcurrent and short-circuit protection devices for lighting, appliance, or power distribution branch circuits.

_____ **28.** Fuses can be checked using a(n) ___ placed across a fuse that has been removed from a circuit.

_____ **29.** A(n) ___ receives incoming power and delivers it to the control circuit and motor loads.

_____ **30.** A(n) ___ is a device which protects transformers and other electrical equipment from voltage surges caused by lightning.

Power Distribution Systems

Worksheet 11-1

Name _____ Date _____

Start/Stop Circuit Control

Complete the wiring diagram according to the line diagram. Do not make any wire splices or additional terminal connections on the wiring diagram. All connections must run from terminal screw to terminal screw.

1. Wire the blank motor control panel as a standard start/stop pushbutton control with memory and an indicating light. Connect the wiring of the motor control panel to the terminal blocks. Use blank spaces adjoining the pushbutton and indicator light to indicate by number which terminals would be connected to these points. For example, the stop pushbutton is marked with wire numbers 1 and 2.

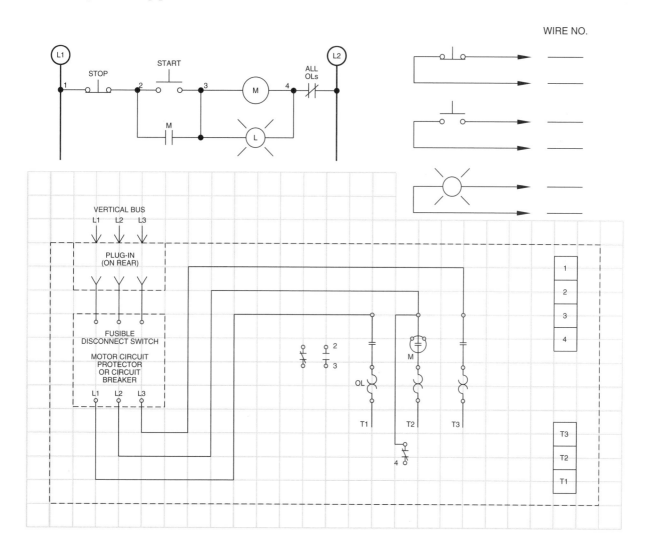

Power Distribution Systems

Worksheet 11-2

Name _____ Date _____

Jogging Circuit Control

Complete the wiring diagram according to the line diagram. Do not make any wire splices or additional terminal connections on the wiring diagram. All connections must run from terminal screw to terminal screw.

1. Wire the blank motor control panel as a jogging circuit with a control relay. Connect the wiring of the motor control panel to the terminal blocks provided. Use blank spaces adjoining the control devices to indicate by number which terminals would be connected to these points.

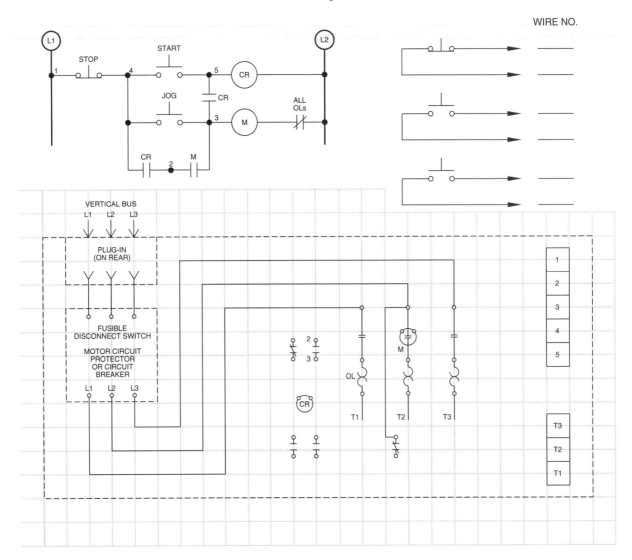

Power Distribution Systems

Name _____   Date _____

Surge and Backspin Protection

Complete the wiring diagram according to the line diagram. Do not make any wire splices or additional terminal connections on the wiring diagram. All connections must run from terminal screw to terminal screw.

1. Wire the blank motor control panel as a circuit that provides surge and backspin protection by means of a time-delay relay. Use the blank spaces adjoining the control devices to indicate by number which terminals would be connected to these points.

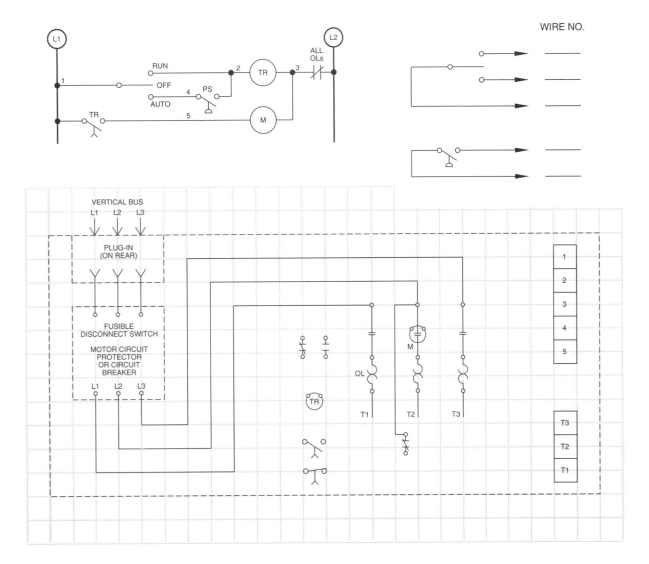

Solid-State Devices and System Integration

Tech-Chek 12

Name _____ Date _____

Electrical Motor Controls

_____ 1. ___ on a PC board are small, round conductors to which component leads are soldered.

_____ 2. ___ are used to interconnect two or more pads.

_____ 3. A(n) ___ is a PC board with multiple terminations on one end.

_____ 4. The ___ is the central core of an atom.

_____ 5. ___ is the addition of impurities to the crystal structure of a semiconductor.

_____ 6. The ___ is the junction of P-type and N-type materials in a diode.

_____ 7. A(n) ___ is a temperature-sensitive resistor.

_____ 8. A(n) ___ converts solar energy into electrical energy.

_____ 9. A(n) ___ is a transducer that changes resistance with a corresponding change in pressure.

_____ 10. ___ is the ratio of the amplitude of an output signal to the amplitude of the input signal.

_____ 11. ___ is the maximum reverse bias voltage that a diode can withstand.
A. Forward current   C. Peak inverse voltage
B. Reverse current   D. Depletion region

_____ 12. A(n) ___ is used to provide conduction from several sources on a PC board.
A. edge card   C. trace
B. bus   D. pad

_____ 13. ___ are free electrons in any conductor.
A. Neutrons   C. Foils
B. Carriers   D. Diodes

_____ 14. ___ current is the minimum current necessary for an SCR to continue conducting.
A. Avalanche   C. Breakover
B. Blocking   D. Holding

_____ 15. A(n) ___ provides a complete circuit function in one semiconductor package.
A. triac   C. integrated circuit
B. diac   D. breakover diac

_____ 16. ___ electrons are the electrons in the outermost shell of an atom.

_____ **17.** ___ are the missing electrons in the crystal structure of a semiconductor.

_____ **18.** ___ devices are devices in which electrical conductivity is between that of a conductor and that of an insulator.

_____ **19.** ___ are electronic components that allow current to pass through them in only one direction.

_____ **20.** A 3ϕ rectifier circuit uses six diodes to produce a(n) ___ circuit with a neutral tap.

_____ **21.** A photovoltaic cell is also known as a(n) ___.

_____ **22.** ___ sensors detect the proximity of a magnetic field.

_____ **23.** A(n) ___ pin is a metal extension from the case of a transistor.

_____ **24.** ___ is the process of taking a small signal and making it larger.

_____ **25.** One advantage of a triac is that virtually no ___ is wasted by being converted to heat.

_____ **26.** A(n) ___ is a very high-gain, directly-coupled amplifier.

_____ **27.** A(n) ___ is an electronic circuit having two stable states designated set and reset.

_____ **28.** A(n) ___ gate may be used in an elevator control circuit to ensure that the elevator cannot move unless the inner and outer doors are closed.

_____ **29.** ___ consist of an IRED input stage and a silicon NPN phototransistor as the output stage.

_____ **30.** Protons carry a(n) ___ charge.

_____ **31.** ___ carry no electrical charge.

_____ **32.** Electrons carry a(n) ___ charge.

_____ **33.** ___ determine the conductive or insulative value of a given material.

_____ **34.** The two types of material created by the addition of new atoms into a crystal are N-type and ___ material.

_____ **35.** ___ flow is equal to and opposite of electron flow.

_____ **36.** ___ is the changing of AC into DC.

_____ **37.** A(n) ___ acts as a voltage regulator either by itself or in conjunction with other semiconductor devices.

_____ **38.** ___ direct current eliminates pulsations and provides direct current at a constant level.

_____ **39.** The three types of transistor amplifiers are the common-emitter, ___, and the ___.

_____ **40.** In any transistor circuit, the ___ junction must always be forward biased and the base/collector junction must always be reverse biased.

_____ **41.** The ___ is the critical factor in determining the amount of current flow in a transistor.

_____ **42.** A transistor switched ON is normally operating in the ___ region.

_____ **43.** When a transistor is switched OFF, it is operating in the ___ region.

_____ **44.** ___ amplifiers are used to obtain additional gain.

_____ **45.** A(n) ___ is a three-electrode AC semiconductor switch that conducts in both directions.

_____ **46.** A(n) ___ transistor is used primarily as a triggering device for SCRs and triacs.

_____ **47.** A(n) ___ is a bidirectional semiconductor that is used primarily as a triggering device.

_____ **48.** ___ are popular because they provide a complete circuit function in one semiconductor package.

_____ **49.** A(n) ___ amplifier is a very high-gain, directly-coupled amplifier that uses external feedback to control response characteristics.

_____ **50.** A(n) ___ gate is a device with an output that is high only when both of its inputs are high.

_____ **51.** A(n) ___ gate is a device with an output that is high if either or both inputs are high.

_____ **52.** A(n) ___ gate is the same as an inverted OR function.

_____ **53.** A(n) ___ gate is the same as an inverted AND function.

_____ **54.** A(n) ___ is an integrated circuit designed to output timing pulses for control of certain types of circuits.

_____ **55.** ___ are the smallest building blocks of matter.
    A. Atoms   C. Electrons
    B. Molecules   D. none of the above

_____ **56.** ___ current is current passed when a diode breaks down.
    A. Breakover   C. Blocking
    B. Avalanche   D. Holding

_____ **57.** A(n) ___ is a circuit containing a diode which permits only the positive half-cycles of the AC sine wave to pass.

_____ **58.** A(n) ___ is the area on a semiconductor material between the P-type and N-type material.

_____ **59.** A(n) ___ is a device which conducts current when energized by light.

_____ **60.** A(n) ___ is a diode which is switched ON and OFF by light.

_____ **61.** A(n) ___ is a three-terminal device that controls current through the device depending on the amount of voltage applied to the base.

_____ **62.** A(n) ___ is a solid-state rectifier with the ability to rapidly switch heavy currents.

_____ **63.** ___ voltage is the voltage required to switch an SCR into a conductive state.

_____ **64.** ___ is a technology that uses a thin flexible glass or plastic fiber to transmit light.

_____ **65.** ___ light is light that is not visible to the human eye.

_____ **66.** A good diode has a(n) ___ drop across it when it is forward biased and conducting current.

_____ **67.** A(n) ___ should be tested using an oscilloscope if the device is suspected of being open.

_____ **68.** A light emitting diode, infrared emitting diode, or ___ diode are light sources for fiber-optic cables.

_____ **69.** A(n)___ rectifier circuit uses six diodes connected to a wye circuit to produce DC.

_____ **70.** Transistors were mainly developed to replace ___ switches.

Solid-State Component Identification

_____ **1.** Thermistor

_____ **2.** Photoconductive cell

_____ **3.** Photovoltaic cell

_____ **4.** Photoconductive diode

_____ **5.** Hall effect sensor

_____ **6.** Solid-state pressure sensor

_____ **7.** Laser diode

_____ **8.** Pin photodiode

_____ **9.** Phototransistor

_____ **10.** Light-activated SCR

_____ **11.** Phototriac

_____ **12.** Optocoupler

A. Responds to magnetic influence

B. Converts solar energy to electrical energy

C. A thermally sensitive resistor

D. Changes resistance with pressure

E. A light-sensitive resistor

F. A light-sensitive diode

G. Combines effect of photodiode and transistor

H. Light sensitive gate and bidirectional

I. Provides electrical isolation between circuits

J. LASCR

K. Produces coherent light

L. Light radiation disturbs the PN junction

Solid-State Devices and System Integration

Worksheet 12-1

Name _____   Date _____

PC Boards

_____   **1.** Insulated board

_____   **2.** Traces

_____   **3.** Terminal contacts

_____   **4.** Pads

_____   **5.** Bus

_____   **6.** Edge card connector

_____   **7.** Components

Solid-State Components

_____   **1.** Resistors

_____   **2.** Wafer switch

_____   **3.** Power transformer

_____   **4.** Transistor

_____   **5.** SCR

_____   **6.** Mini-DIP IC

_____   **7.** TO-5 IC

_____   **8.** Trimmer resistor

_____   **9.** Capacitor

_____   **10.** Dual inline IC

_____   **11.** Large-scale IC

_____   **12.** Heat sink

_____   **13.** DIP switch

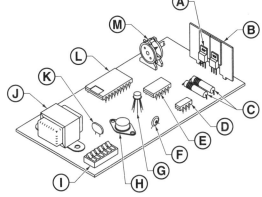

Solid-State Devices and System Integration

Worksheet 12-2

Name _____ Date _____

Diode Operation

_____ **1.** Forward-bias voltage

_____ **2.** Reverse breakdown

_____ **3.** Reverse-bias voltage

_____ **4.** Reverse current

_____ **5.** Forward operating current

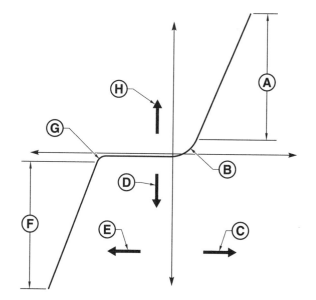

Zener Diode Operation

_____ **1.** Zener breakdown

_____ **2.** Forward breakover voltage

_____ **3.** Forward current

_____ **4.** Standard diode operating range

_____ **5.** Reverse-bias voltage

_____ **6.** Forward-bias voltage

_____ **7.** Zener diode operating range

_____ **8.** Reverse current

Solid-State Devices and System Integration

Worksheet 12-3

Name _____   Date _____

SCR Operation

_____ **1.** Forward breakover voltage

_____ **2.** Holding current

_____ **3.** Reverse breakdown voltage

_____ **4.** Avalanche current

_____ **5.** Reverse current

_____ **6.** Forward blocking current

Amplifiers

1. Connect the load to the common-emitter amplifier.

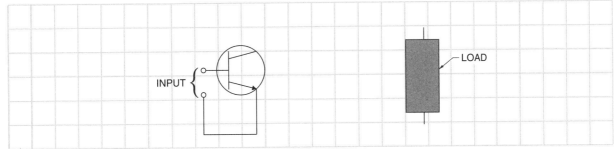

2. Connect the load to the common-base amplifier.

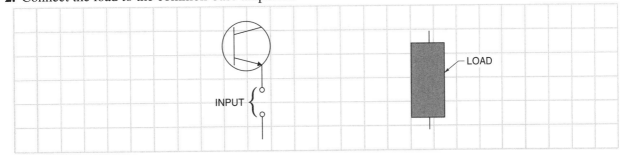

Solid-State Devices and System Integration

Name _____ Date _____

Solid-State Devices

1. Complete the schematic for the 555 timer and label each part.

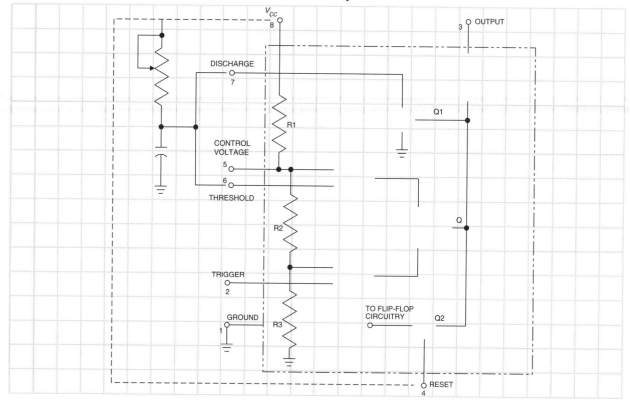

2. Indicate the direction of current flow through the full-wave bridge rectifier. A is positive and B is negative with respect to A. D1 and D2 are forward biased and conduct. D3 and D4 are reversed biased and do not conduct.

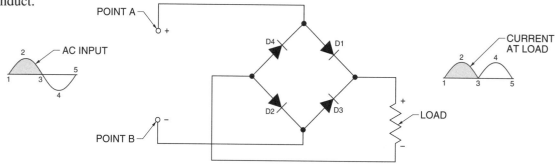

Solid-State Devices and System Integration

Worksheet 12-5

Name _____ Date _____

Solid-State Symbol Identification

_____ 1. SCR

_____ 2. Thermistor

_____ 3. Diode

_____ 4. Optocoupler

_____ 5. Triac

_____ 6. LED

_____ 7. Unijunction transistor

_____ 8. Diac

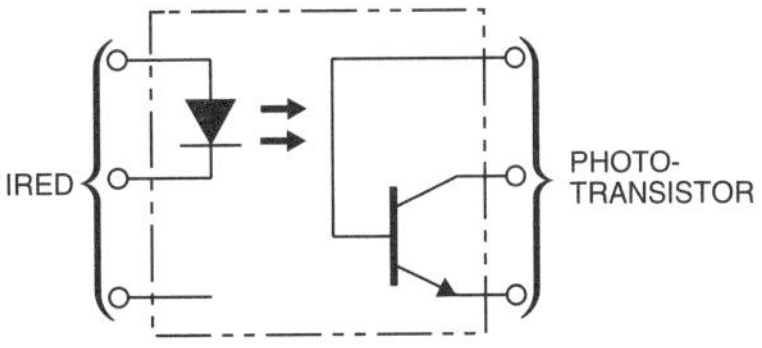

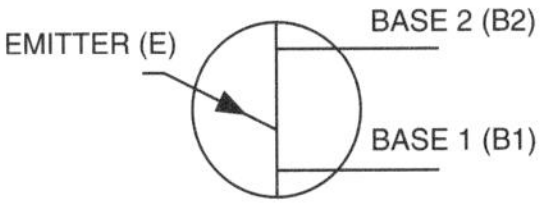

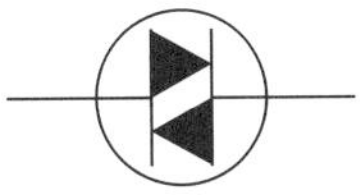

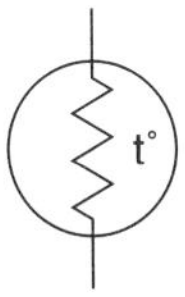

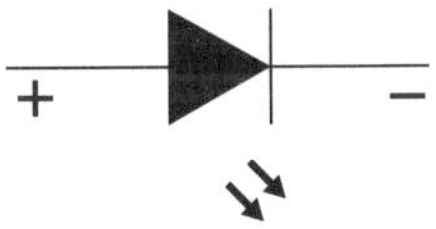

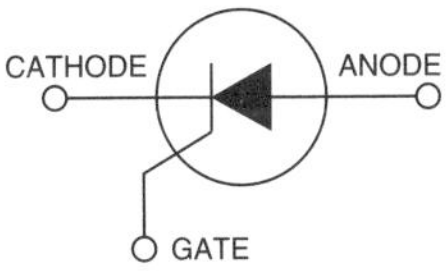

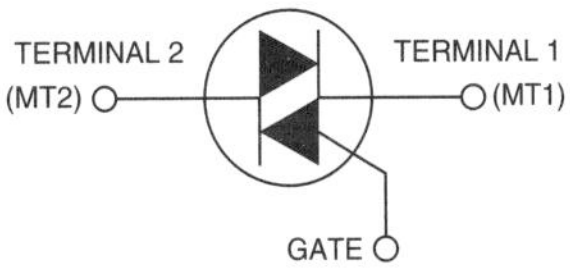

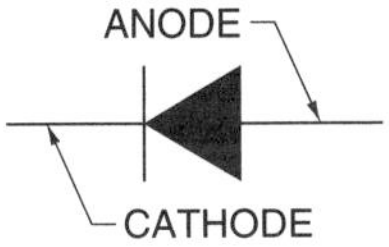

Light-Activated Devices

_____ 1. Photoconductive cell

_____ 2. Photovoltaic cell

_____ 3. Phototransistor

_____ 4. Photoconductive diode

_____ 5. Phototriac

_____ 6. Pin photodiode

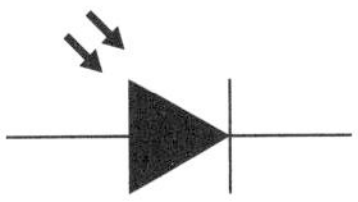

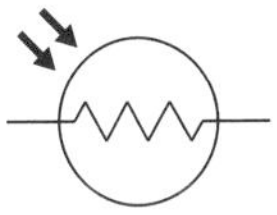

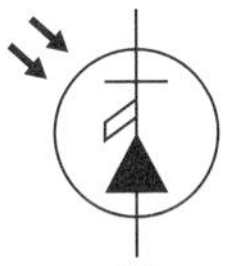

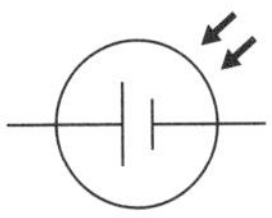

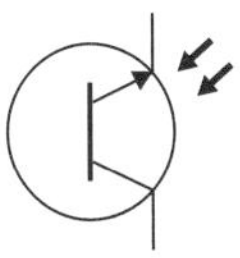

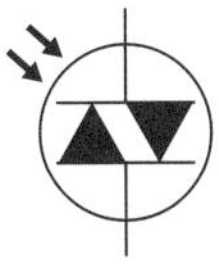

Integrated Circuits

_____ **1.** Dual inline

_____ **2.** Mini-DIP

_____ **3.** TO-5

_____ **4.** MOS/LSI

_____ **5.** Flat-pack

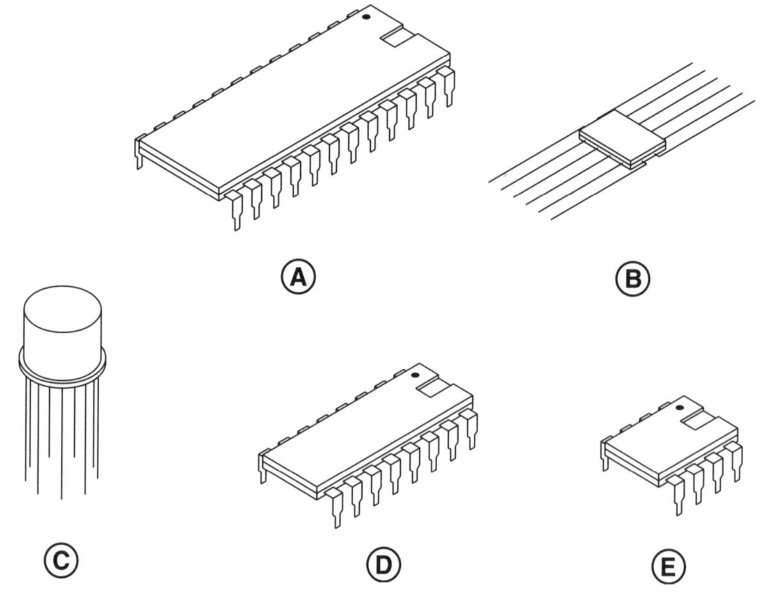

Ⓐ   Ⓑ

Ⓒ   Ⓓ   Ⓔ

Logic Gates

_____ **1.** NAND

_____ **2.** NOR

_____ **3.** OR

_____ **4.** AND

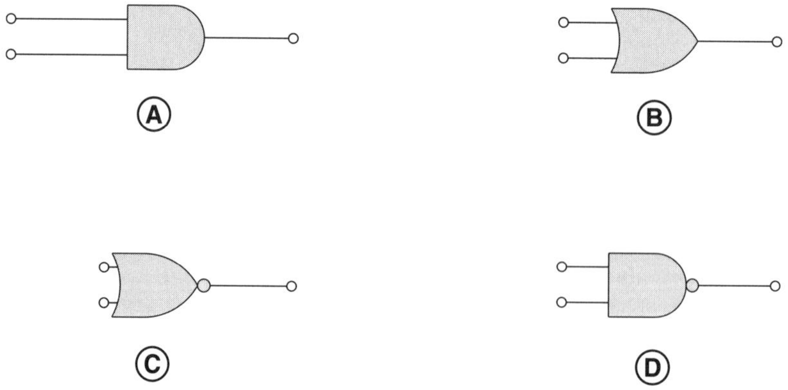

Ⓐ   Ⓑ

Ⓒ   Ⓓ

Transistors

_____ **1.** Base

_____ **2.** Collector

_____ **3.** Emitter

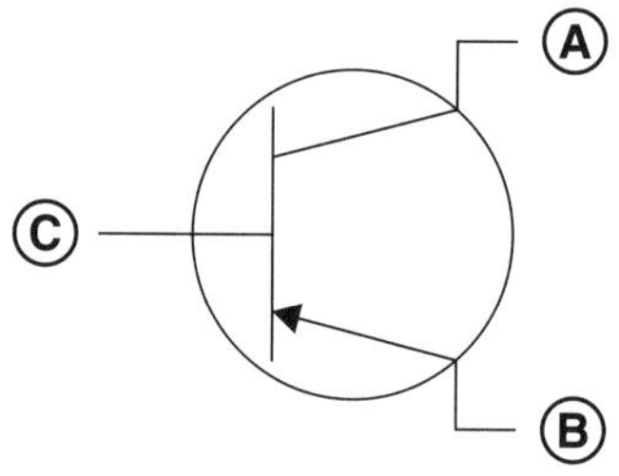

Ⓐ

Ⓒ

Ⓑ

Solid-State Devices and System Integration

Worksheet 12-6

Name _____ Date _____

Digital AND Circuit Logic

1. Wire the pushbuttons to control the motor using the solid-state relay as the interface. Connect the circuit so the motor starts only when Pushbutton 1 and Pushbutton 2 are pressed. Connect the pushbuttons and solid-state relay to the correct terminal blocks. Make all the connections at the terminal blocks. Each terminal block screw is designed to hold up to three wires.

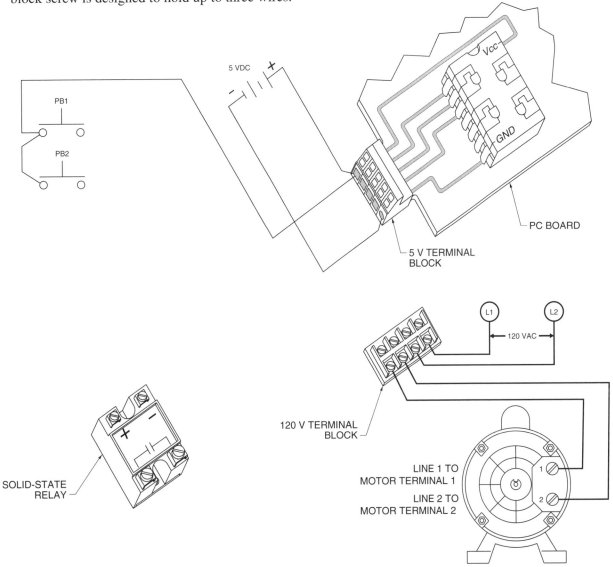

Solid-State Devices and System Integration

Worksheet 12-7

Name _____ Date _____

Digital MEMORY Circuit Logic

1. Wire the pushbuttons to control the motor using the solid-state relay as the interface. Connect the circuit so the motor starts only when Pushbutton 1 and Pushbutton 2 are pressed together or when Pushbutton 3 is pressed. Connect the pushbuttons and solid-state relay to the correct terminal blocks. Make all the connections at the terminal blocks. Each terminal block screw is designed to hold up to three wires. *Note:* Connect only one output from a gate to the relay. Do not connect the gate outputs in parallel.

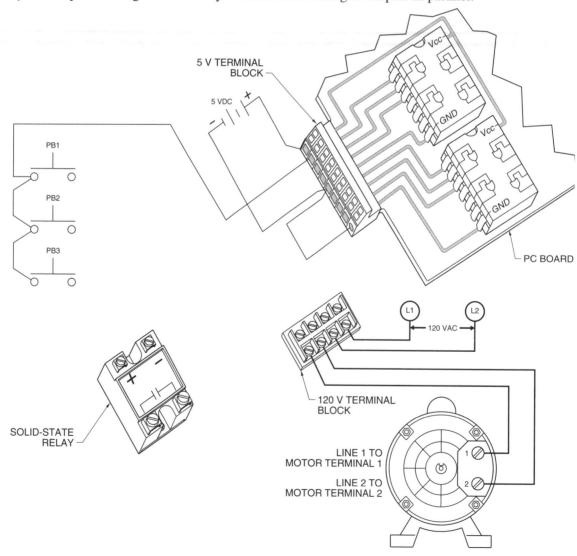

![Solid-State Devices and System Integration — Worksheet 12-8]

Solid-State Devices and System Integration

Worksheet 12-8

Name _____ Date _____

Digital NOT Circuit Logic

1. Wire the pushbuttons to control the motor using the solid-state relay as the interface. Connect the circuit so the motor starts only when Pushbutton 1 is pressed and the limit switch is not activated. Connect the pushbuttons and solid-state relay to the correct terminal blocks. Make all the connections at the terminal blocks. Each terminal block screw is designed to hold up to three wires.

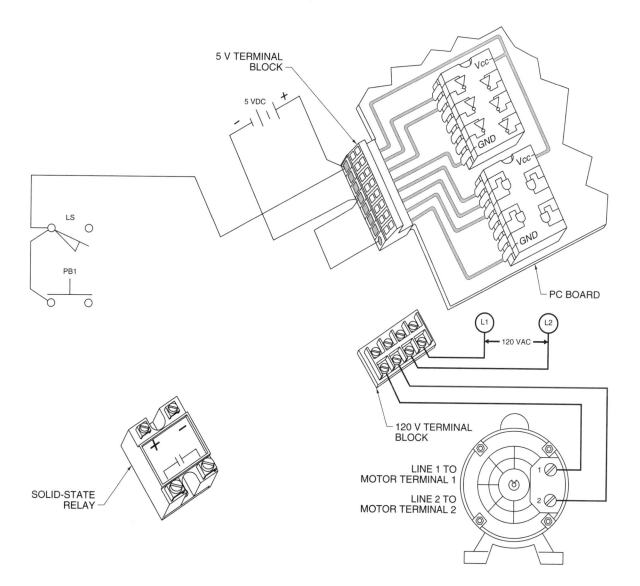

Solid-State Devices and System Integration

Worksheet 12-9

Name _____ Date _____

Digital Combination Circuit Logic

1. Wire the pushbuttons to control the motor using the solid-state relay as the interface. Connect the circuit so the motor starts only when the start pushbutton is pressed and released and stops when the stop pushbutton is pressed. Connect the pushbuttons and solid-state relay to the correct terminal blocks. Make all connections at the terminal blocks. Each terminal block screw is designed to hold up to three wires.

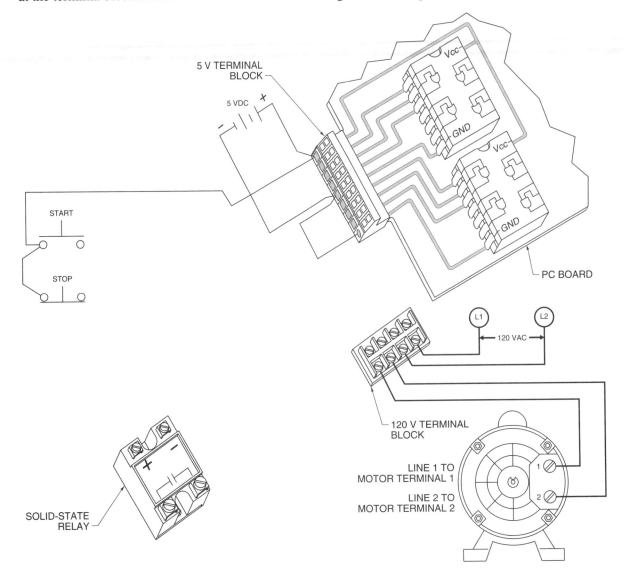

Timers and Counters

Tech-Chek 13

Name _____ Date _____

Electrical Motor Controls

_____ 1. A(n) ___ is a solid-state control device that controls an industrial process or machine.

_____ 2. A(n) ___ is a timer that maintains its current accumulated time value when its control input is interrupted or removed.

_____ 3. A(n) ___ is a timer that does not maintain its current accumulated time value when its control input is interrupted or removed.

_____ 4. A(n) ___ is a device in which the contacts change position immediately and remain changed for the set period of time after the timer has received power.

_____ 5. A(n) ___ is a timer that operates with equal ON and OFF time periods.

_____ 6. A(n) ___ is a timer that is controlled by an external transistor from a separately powered electronic circuit.

_____ 7. A(n) ___ is a timer controlled by an external sensor in which the timer supplies the power required to operate the sensor.

_____ 8. A(n) ___ is a device used to count inputs and provide an output (contacts) after the preset count value is reached.

_____ 9. A(n) ___ is a counting device that keeps track of the total number of inputs and displays the counted value.

_____ 10. A(n) ___ is a device used to count inputs from two different inputs.

_____ 11. ___ diagrams are the actual diagrams which match the logic of manufactured product line diagrams.

_____ 12. ___ timers are used in applications that require a load to remain energized even after the input control has been removed.

_____ 13. Four major categories of timers are ___, ___, ___, and ___.
   A. ON-delay; OFF-delay; one-shot; recycle
   B. dashpot; ON-delay; OFF-delay; solid-state
   C. programmable; ON-delay; OFF-delay; synchronous clock
   D. dashpot; synchronous clock; solid-state; programmable

_____ 14. A(n) ___ circuit provides a very accurate timing function at the most economical cost.

Operational Diagrams

1. Complete the operational diagram so that it illustrates an ON-delay operation.

2. Complete the operational diagram so that it illustrates an OFF-delay operation.

3. Complete the operational diagram so that it illustrates a one-shot operation.

4. Complete the operational diagram so that it illustrates a recycle operation.

Timers

Refer to Timer Socket for questions 1-3.

_____ **1.** The coil voltage is applied to pins ___.

_____ **2.** The normally open contacts are pins ___ and 11 and 9.

_____ **3.** The normally closed contacts are pins ___ and 11 and 8.

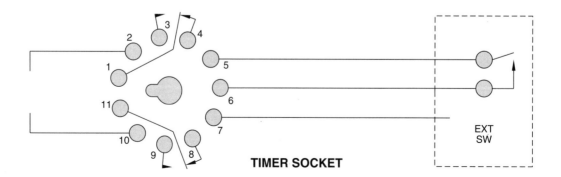

TIMER SOCKET

Timing Codes

Add the timing code (X and O) for each load.

_____ **1.** Load 1 timing code is ___.

_____ **2.** Load 2 timing code is ___.

_____ **3.** Load 3 timing code is ___.

_____ **4.** Load 4 timing code is ___.

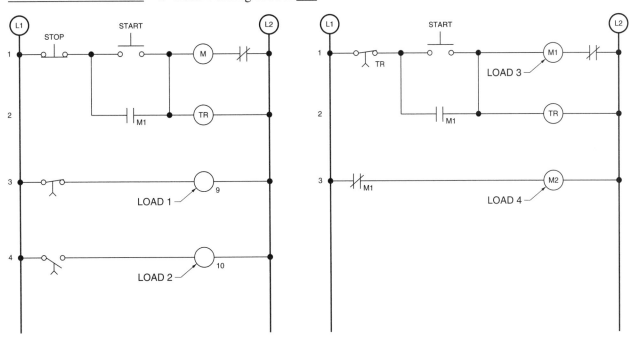

Timer Contact Symbols

1. Draw the symbol for a normally open timed-closed contact.

⭕   ⭕

2. Draw the symbol for a normally closed, timed-open contact.

⭕   ⭕

3. Draw the symbol for a normally open timed-open contact.

⭕   ⭕

4. Draw the symbol for a normally closed timed-closed contact.

⭕   ⭕

Timers and Counters

Name _____ Date _____

ON-Delay Motor Sequencing

The circuit is a start/stop pushbutton station with memory controlling two motors. A time-delay relay prevents both motors from starting simultaneously. An overload in Motor 1 shuts down the entire circuit. An overload in Motor 2 affects only Motor 2. This circuit is often used because incoming power line limitations in some areas prohibit the starting of two or more motors simultaneously.

1. Complete the wiring diagram for the line diagram. Do not make any wire splices or additional terminal connections on the wiring diagram. All connections must run from terminal screw to terminal screw.

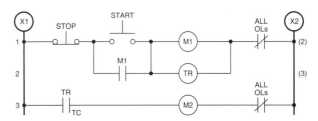

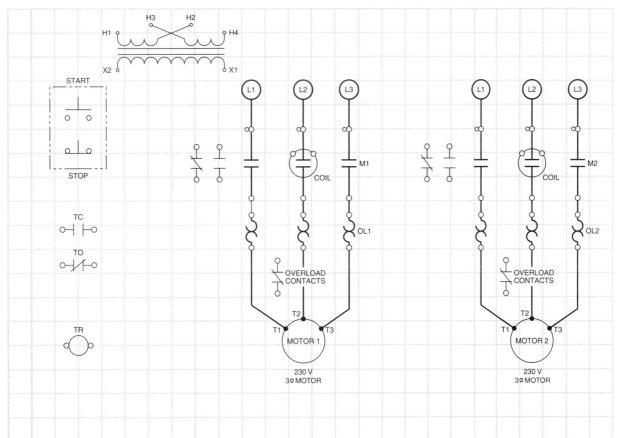

Timers and Counters

Worksheet 13-2

Name _____ Date _____

OFF-Delay Motor Control

In the circuit, Motor 2 starts and runs for a short time after Motor 1 has stopped. An overload in Motor 1 shuts down the entire circuit. An overload in Motor 2 affects only Motor 2. This circuit is used when a second motor is to run for a short time after the controlling motor has stopped, as in a cooling fan or pump.

1. Complete the wiring diagram for the line diagram. Do not make any wire splices or additional terminal connections on the wiring diagram. All connections must run from terminal screw to terminal screw.

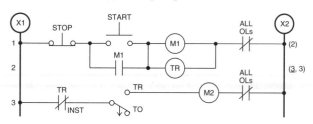

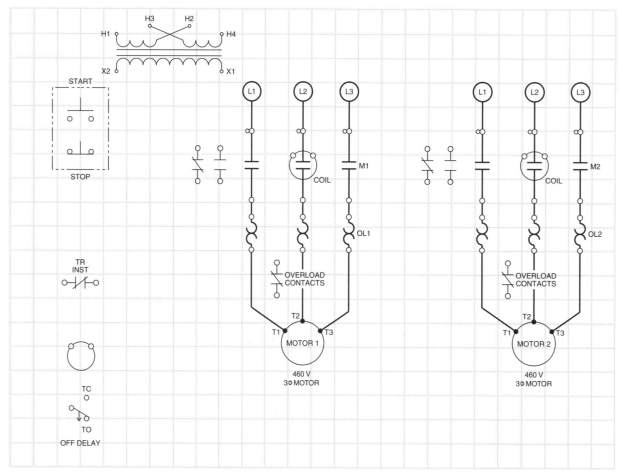

Timers and Counters

Name _____   Date _____

Timer Coding

1. Use Data Sheet E on page 263 to complete the line diagram for the six circuits based on their established coding system for the load.

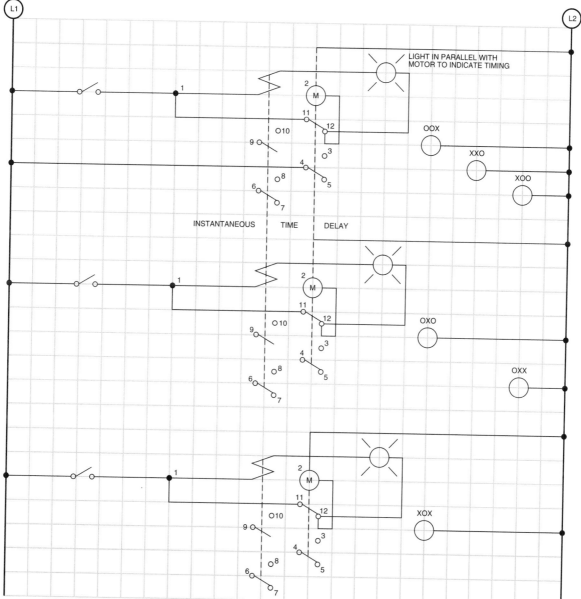

Timers and Counters

Worksheet 13-4

Name _____   Date _____

Timer Motor Sequencing

A conveyor system is to be installed in which the first conveyor (controlled by M1) is turned ON by a standard start pushbutton with memory. After the first conveyor has run for 1 min, a second conveyor (controlled by M2) turns ON automatically. Both conveyors run until a standard stop pushbutton causes both to stop. Each conveyor motor should have independent overload protection.

1. Use Data Sheet F on page 265 to complete the timing circuit line diagram. Use standard lettering, numbering, and coding information.

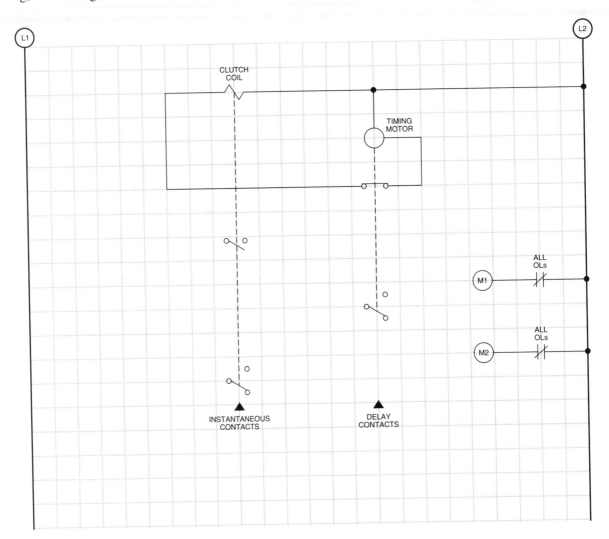

Timers and Counters

Name _____ Date _____

Timer Safety Circuit

A time control is to be installed to operate a sandblasting machine. A part is automatically sandblasted for 30 sec when the operator places the part in the machine, closes the door, and turns on a toggle switch. The sandblaster is powered by a motor (controlled by M1). During sandblasting, a red pilot light illuminates, indicating danger. At all other times, a green pilot light illuminates, indicating it is safe to open the door. Overload protection should be provided for the motor.

1. Use Data Sheet F on page 265 to complete the timing circuit line diagrams. Use standard lettering, numbering, and coding information.

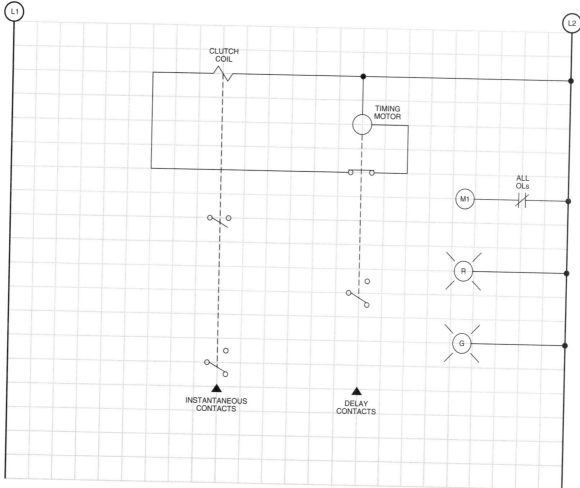

CIRCUIT 1

2. Redraw the sandblasting circuit so that a pushbutton may be built into the door of the machine to turn OFF the sandblasting operation any time the door is open.

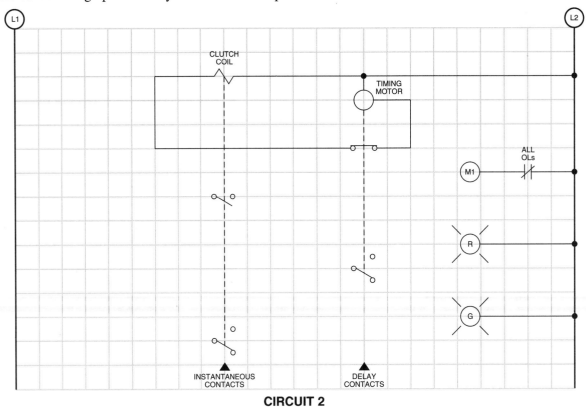

CIRCUIT 2

3. Redraw Circuit 2 so no sandblasting can take place unless the operator holds two pushbuttons down during the sandblasting operation.

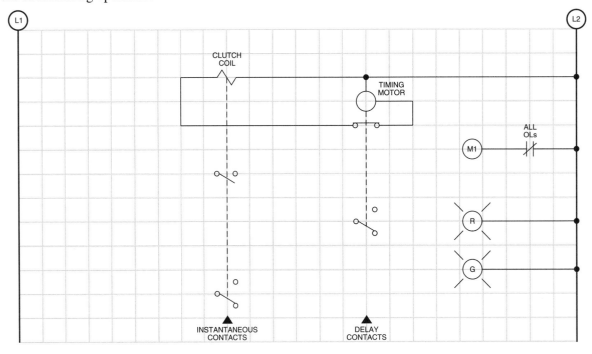

Timers and Counters

Worksheet 13-6

Name _____ Date _____

ON-Delay Timer Operational Diagrams

Complete the operational diagram for each load in the circuit.

1.

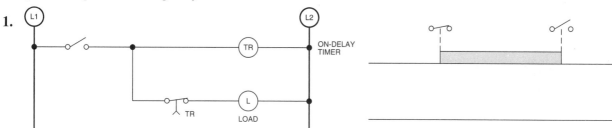

2.

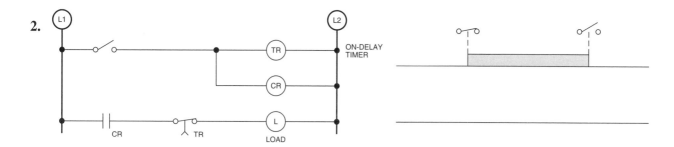

3.

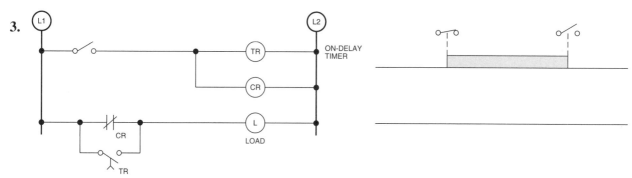

4.

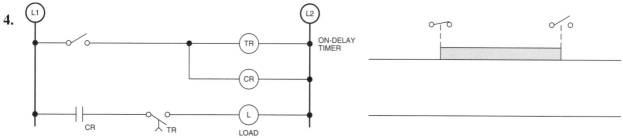

Timers and Counters

Name _____   Date _____

Release Delay Relay – Sequential Control

1. Draw the line diagram of the wiring diagram.

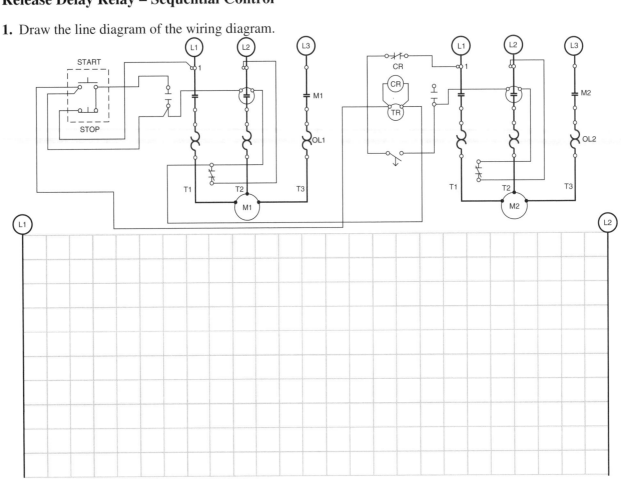

Answer the questions using the information and Sequential Control Circuit. Motor Starter 1 controls a pump motor. Motor Starter 2 controls a fan motor. The timer is set for 5 min.

_____   **2.** Motor ___ starts first after the start button is pressed.

_____   **3.** Does the other motor start after 5 min?

_____   **4.** Motor ___ starts after the stop button is pressed.

_____   **5.** Do both motors ever run at the same time?

_____   **6.** Do both motors ever stop at the same time?

Timers and Counters

Worksheet 13-8

Name _____ Date _____

Recycle Timer

1. Draw the line diagram of a control circuit using the Data Sheet G recycle timer on page 266 so the timer starts running when a two-position selector switch is placed in the automatic position. The timer is set for a 4 min OFF-delay period. After the 4 min, the timer contacts energize a solenoid. The solenoid controls the lubrication flow. After a short ON-time period, the timer turns OFF the solenoid for another 4 min. When the selector switch is placed in the OFF position, the timer stops running. Mark the timer pin numbers on the circuit.

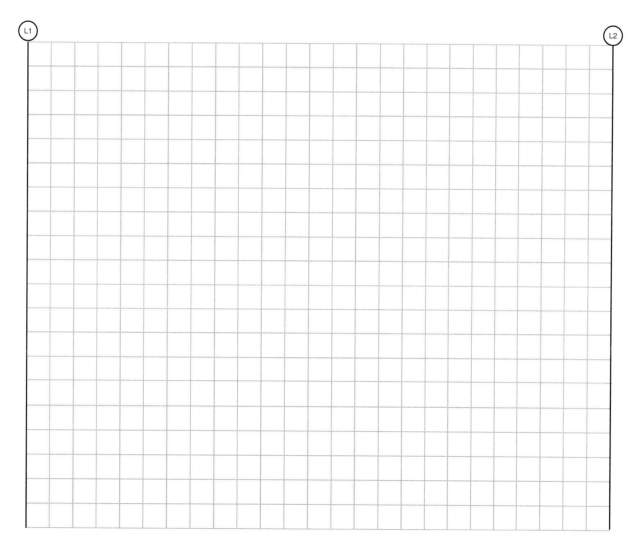

Timers and Counters

Worksheet 13-9

Name _____ Date _____

Combination Timing Logic

Timers are combined for sensitive heat control. Timer 1 is set for 2 min and timer 2 is set for 5 min. Timer 1 ensures the heater is ON for at least 2 min, even if the temperature switch opens before 2 min. Timer 2 prevents the heater from turning back ON for at least 5 min, even if the temperature switch closes. This combination ensures an even and economical heat supply.

1. Draw the line diagram for the circuit using the Data Sheet H operate delay relay on page 267 and the Data Sheet I release delay relay on page 268.

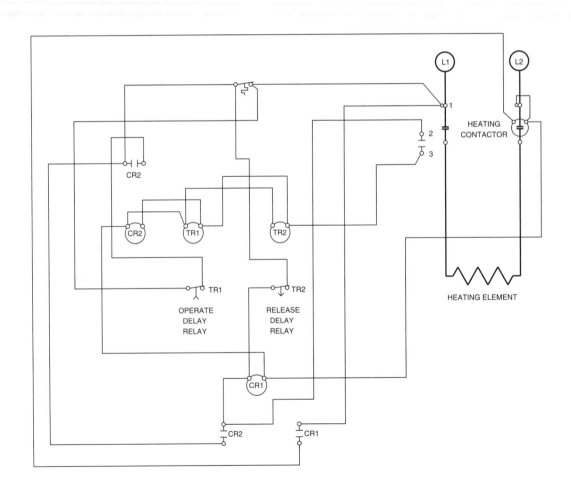

L1

L2

Timers and Counters

Name _____ Date _____

Operate Delay Relays

A current monitor can be used to detect blade wear. As the blade wears, the drive motor draws more current. When the current reaches a set limit, the current monitor activates the contacts. The current monitor uses a current transformer to detect the amount of motor current. By using different current transformers, currents from .1 A to 500 A can be detected.

1. Draw the line diagram of the saw blade control circuit using a standard start/stop pushbutton station. Use a magnetic motor starter to control the motor and a start/stop pushbutton station to control the motor starter. Use the motor starter overload contact for overload protection. Do not include the current monitor in the line diagram.

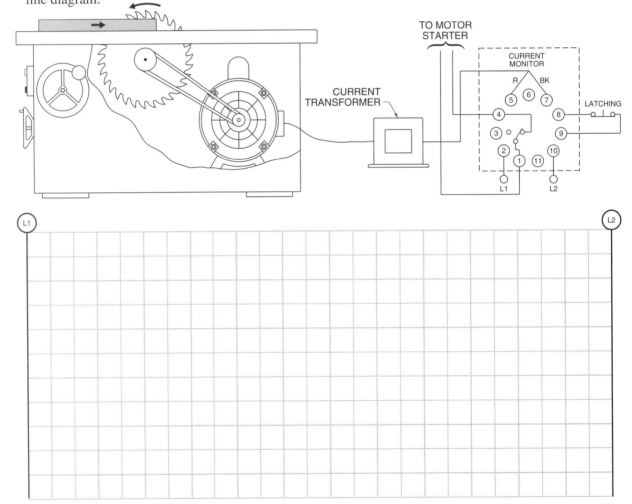

In the saw blade control circuit, the motor starter overload contact stops the motor when a sustained overload oc-curs. The additional current drawn as the saw blade wears is not detected by the motor starter overload. To detect the additional current, a current monitor is used. A current monitor is set to detect a current higher than normal, but lower than a sustained overload. The current monitor has no built-in time delay. Because all motors draw higher-than-normal current when starting, an operate delay relay is used with a current monitor in motor circuits. The operate delay relay prevents the current monitor from de-energizing the motor starter during normal motor startup.

2. Redraw the saw blade control circuit line diagram, adding the current monitor and an operate delay relay from Data Sheet H on page 267. Add the current monitor so the motor starter is de-energized when the current monitor detects blade wear. Add the operate delay relay to prevent the current monitor contacts from de-energizing the starter during normal motor startup. Mark all terminal connections from the current monitor and operate delay relay. The current monitor is set for 4 A and the overload contacts are set for 6 A. Mark the operate delay relay setting for 5 sec.

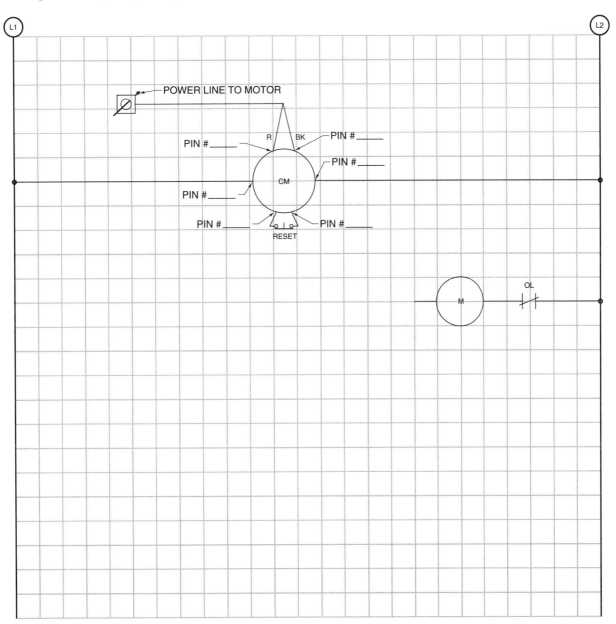

In the saw blade control circuit with current monitor, the motor is de-energized if a sustained overload or blade wear occurs (de-energized by the overload contact and the current monitor, respectively). When the overloads de-energize the motor, the motor can be restarted because the overload contact automatically resets. When the current monitor de-energizes the motor, the motor can only be restarted after the reset pushbutton connected to the current monitor is pressed.

3. Redraw the saw blade control circuit with current monitor adding a light that energizes when the current monitor de-energizes the motor. The light indicates the blade is worn and the current monitor stopped the motor. Use the Data Sheet G recycle timer on page 266 to flash the light ON and OFF. Mark all terminal connections.

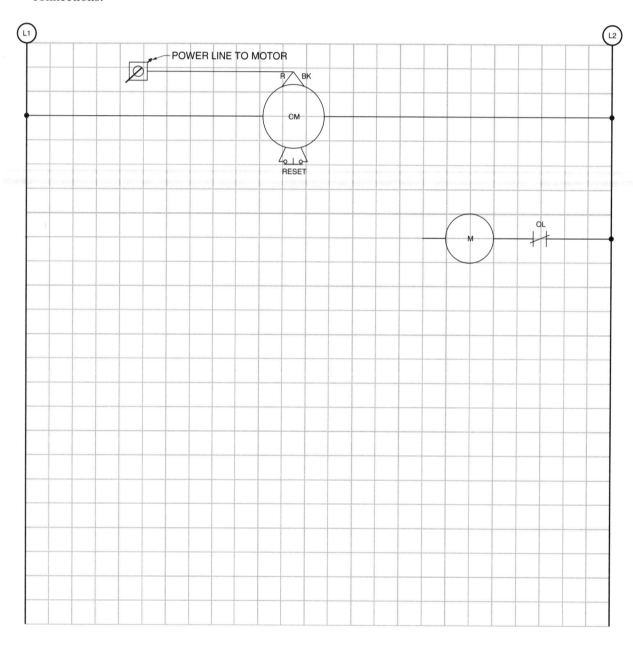

Relays and Solid-State Starters

Tech-Chek 14

Name _____   Date _____

Electrical Motor Controls

_____ 1. A ___ is the number of completely isolated circuits a relay can switch at one time.
    A. throw   C. make
    B. pole   D. break

_____ 2. A ___ is the number of closed contact positions per pole.
    A. throw   C. make
    B. pole   D. break

_____ 3. A ___ is the number of separate places on a contact that open or close an electrical circuit.
    A. throw   C. make
    B. pole   D. break

_____ 4. A(n) ___ relay is used to ramp up the voltage applied to a load.
    A. reed   C. instant ON switching
    B. general-purpose   D. analog switching

_____ 5. A(n) ___ relay is an SSR that turns ON a load when the voltage at the load crosses near or at the zero point.
    A. reed   C. machine control
    B. instant ON switching   D. zero switching

_____ 6. A(n) ___ relay is normally a plug-in relay and does not have convertible or replaceable contacts.
    A. reed   C. instant ON switching
    B. general-purpose   D. peak switching

_____ 7. A(n) ___ relay normally includes replaceable, convertible, or interchangeable contacts.
    A. analog switching   C. general-purpose
    B. machine control   D. zero switching

_____ 8. A(n) ___ relay is activated by the presence of a magnetic field.
    A. reed   C. instant ON switching
    B. general-purpose   D. peak switching

_____ 9. A(n) ___ relay is an SSR that allows the load to be turned ON at any point on the AC sine wave.
    A. reed   C. instant ON switching
    B. peak switching   D. zero switching

_____ 10. A(n) ___ relay's contacts are sealed and impervious to dust, humidity, and fumes, and have a long service life.
    A. reed   B. general-purpose
    C. instant ON switching   D. peak switching

_____ 11. Relay manufacturers use a common ___ to simplify the identification of relays.

_____ 12. Typical contact life ratings for electromechanical relays are between ___ and ___ operations.

_____ 13. Typical mechanical life ratings for electromechanical relays are between ___ and ___ operations.

_____ 14. A(n) ___ is a circuit that protects contacts by providing a nondestructive path for generated voltage as a switch is opened.

_____ 15. A(n) ___ is a resistor whose resistance is inversely proportional to the voltage applied to it.

_____ 16. ___ is the ability of a device to impede the flow of heat.

_____ 17. An advantage of an EMR is ___.
    A. poor performance when switching high inrush currents   C. short contact life when used for rapid switching applications or high current loads
    B. very low contact voltage drop, requiring no heat sink   D. none of the above

_____ 18. A limitation of EMRs is ___.
    A. no OFF-state leakage current through open contacts   C. they generate EMI on power lines
    B. they normally have a multi-pole, multithrow contact arrangement   D. their contacts can switch AC or DC

_____ 19. ___ is the trip point from the time the motor starts until the first time the overloads trip.

_____ 20. ___ is the trip point after the overloads have tripped and have been reset.

_____ 21. When a starter is set for ___, the motor is gradually accelerated over a programmable time period.

_____ 22. Motor starting modes include soft stop, pump control, and ___.

_____ 23. ___ are temporary, unwanted voltages in an electrical circuit.

_____ 24. The ___ is a method of SSR replacement in which a logical sequence is used to determine the reason for failure.

_____ 25. ___ is a phenomenon that occurs when a relay fails to turn OFF because the current and voltage in the circuit reach zero at different times.

Reed Relay Actuation

_____ **1.** Parallel motion

_____ **2.** Perpendicular motion

_____ **3.** Shielding

_____ **4.** Pivoted motion

_____ **5.** Rotary motion

_____ **6.** Front-to-back motion

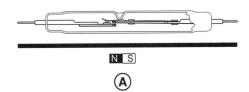

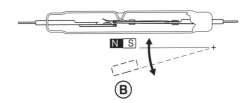

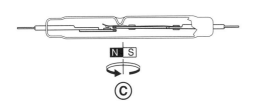

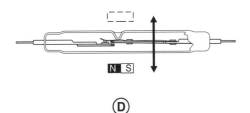

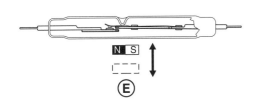

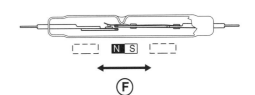

EMR and SSR Comparison

Match the EMR term with the equivalent SSR term.

_____ **1.** Coil voltage

_____ **2.** Coil current

_____ **3.** Pull-in time

_____ **4.** Contact voltage rating

_____ **5.** Contact current rating

_____ **6.** Contact voltage drop

_____ **7.** Insulation resistance

A. Switch-OFF resistance

B. Switch-ON voltage drop

C. Control voltage

D. Load current

E. Load voltage

F. Control current

G. Turn-ON time

Relays and Solid-State Starters

Worksheet 14-1

Name _____ Date _____

Electromechanical Relay Contact Addition

Complete the line diagrams according to the circuit information. Use standard lettering, numbering, and coding information.

1. Design a control circuit so a 24 V pushbutton (ON/OFF with memory) operates an electromechanical relay to control a 230 V solenoid.

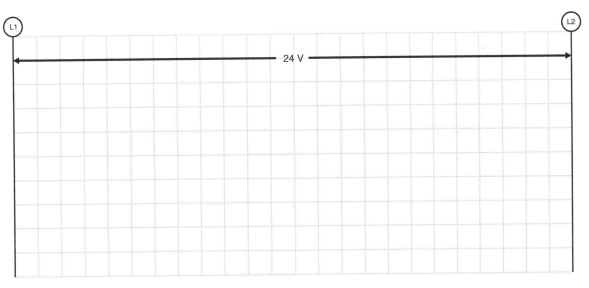

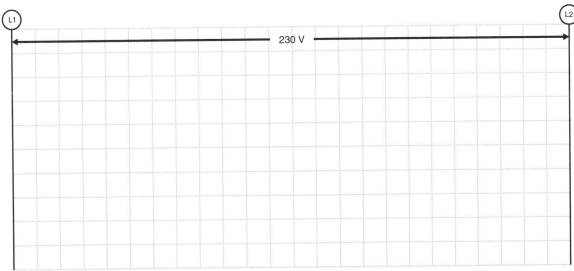

2. Design a control circuit so a magnetic motor starter is activated by a standard start/stop pushbutton station with memory. Add a control relay with three auxiliary contacts to extend the number of contacts available with the motor starter. One set of normally closed contacts is to control a green light, the other set of normally closed contacts is to control a solenoid, and the normally open contacts are to control a red light. Provide overload protection for the motor.

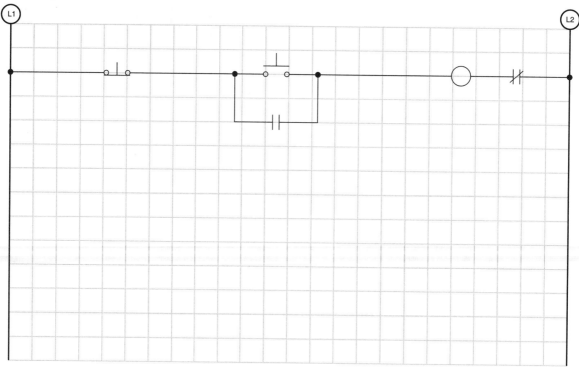

CIRCUIT 1

3. Redraw Circuit 1, adding a 24 VAC relay coil and motor starter coil to control the motor and a 115 VAC green light, red light, and solenoid into the circuit.

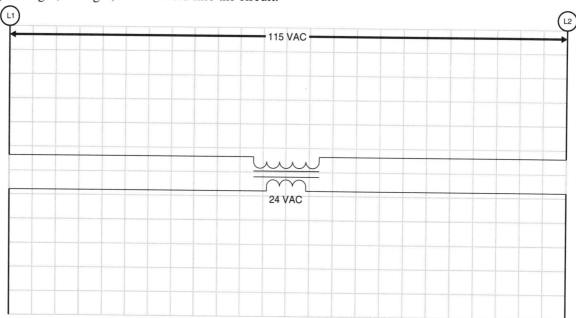

Relays and Solid-State Starters

Worksheet 14-2

Name _____   Date _____

Pole/Throw/Break Identification

Determine the correct number of poles, throws, and breaks for each contact arrangement.

_____ **1.** Poles	_____ **4.** Poles	_____ **7.** Poles
_____ **2.** Throws	_____ **5.** Throws	_____ **8.** Throws
_____ **3.** Breaks	_____ **6.** Breaks	_____ **9.** Breaks

_____ **10.** Poles	_____ **13.** Poles	_____ **16.** Poles
_____ **11.** Throws	_____ **14.** Throws	_____ **17.** Throws
_____ **12.** Breaks	_____ **15.** Breaks	_____ **18.** Breaks

_____ **19.** Poles	_____ **22.** Poles
_____ **20.** Throws	_____ **23.** Throws
_____ **21.** Breaks	_____ **24.** Breaks

Relays and Solid-State Starters

Worksheet 14-3

Name _____ Date _____

Control Circuit Solid-State Relay Use

Complete the control diagrams according to the circuit information. Use standard lettering, numbering, and coding information.

1. Complete the control diagram so it contains a start pushbutton connected for memory to start the motor and a stop pushbutton to stop the motor. Include overload contacts to stop the motor if an overload occurs. Use an SCR for solid-state memory. Include a current-limiting resistor in the gate circuit.

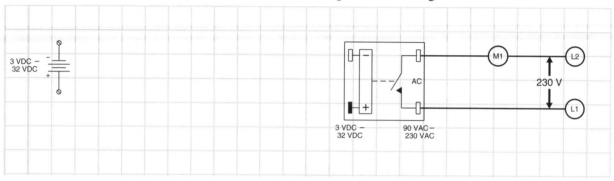

CIRCUIT 1

2. Complete the wiring diagram showing the actual wire placement for Circuit 1.

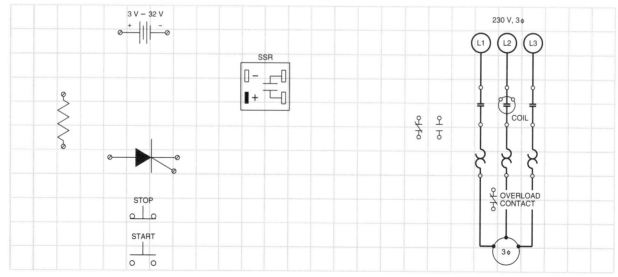

3. Redraw Circuit 1, adding an ON-delay timer to automatically turn OFF the motor after 30 min. The timer has a coil voltage rated at the same voltage level as the magnetic motor starter coil.

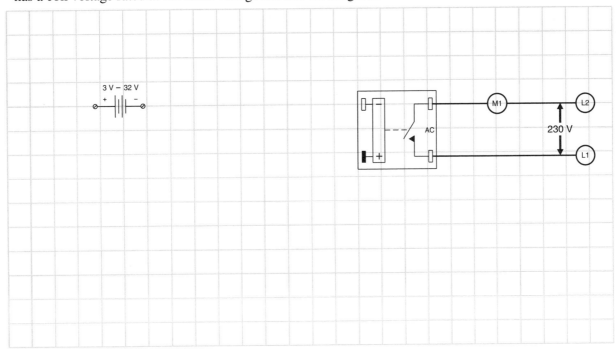

4. Redraw Circuit 1, adding an OFF-delay timer to keep the motor running for 30 min after the stop pushbutton is pressed. The timer has a coil voltage rated at the same voltage level as the magnetic motor starter coil.

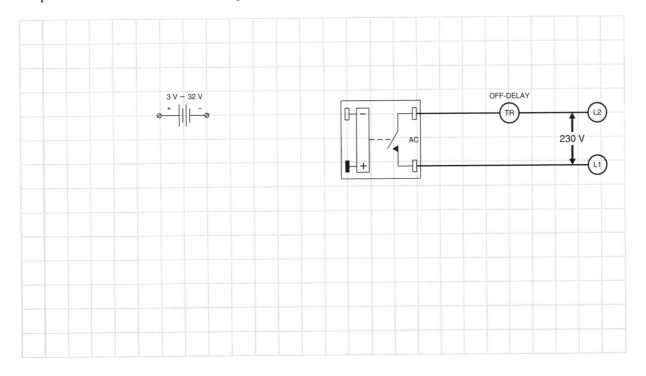

Relays and Solid-State Starters

Worksheet 14-4

Name _____   Date _____

Forward and Reversing Solid-State Relay Use

Complete the control diagram according to the circuit information. Use standard lettering, numbering, and coding information.

1. Design a control circuit using two solid-state relays to forward and reverse a motor. Include a forward/reverse/stop pushbutton and pushbutton interlocking. Use SCRs to add memory in the forward and reverse direction. Include a current-limiting resistor in each gate circuit.

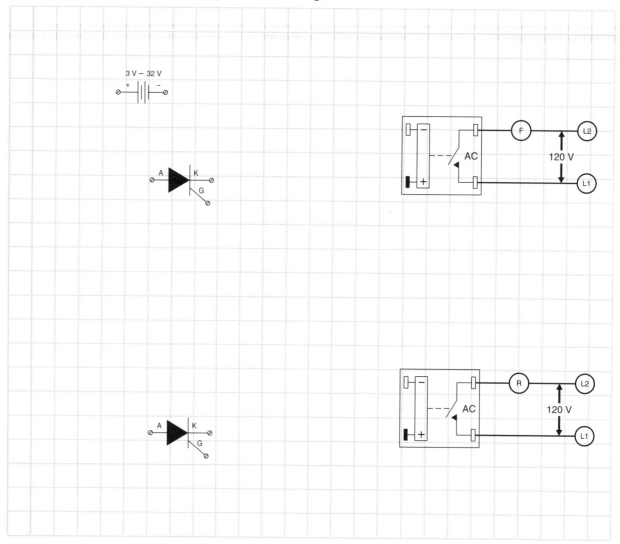

Relays and Solid-State Starters

Worksheet 14-5

Name _____ Date _____

Magnetic Matching Relays

1. Draw the line diagram of the Motor Jog Circuit including a relay that allows the motor to be jogged or started.

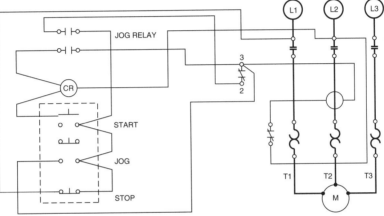

MOTOR JOG CIRCUIT

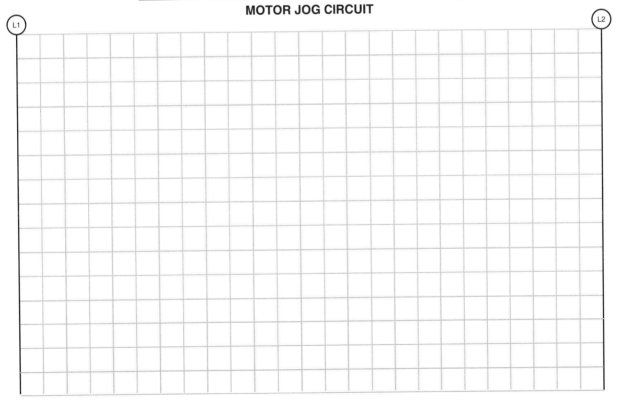

In the Motor Jog Circuit on page 165 using the jog relay, the starter is de-energized when a power failure occurs. The starter does not automatically energize when power is reapplied. To automatically energize a starter after a power failure, a latching relay is used.

2. Redraw the line diagram of the circuit using a jog relay and add an AC coil DPDT latching relay in place of the jog relay. Change the stop button to normally open the stop button. When the start button is used, the starter energizes and remains energized after the start button is pressed and released. When the jog button is used, the starter energizes only as long as the jog button is pressed.

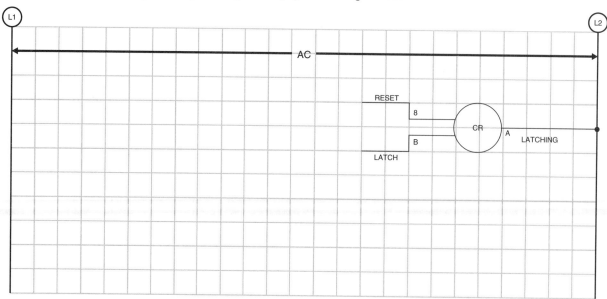

3. Draw a line diagram using the DC, dual-coil, SPST latching relay. An ON button energizes the lamp and a second OFF button de-energizes the lamp. Mark each terminal number used from the latching relay on the line diagram.

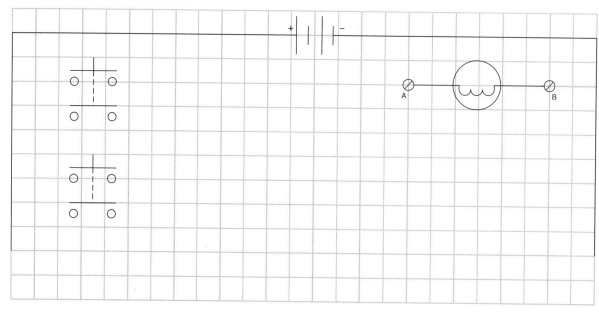

4. Draw a line diagram using the AC coil, 3PDT latching relay. An ON button energizes a motor starter in the AC circuit and a second OFF button de-energizes the starter. Use the first set of contacts (1, 4, 7) to control the starter. Use the second set of contacts to energize a solenoid in the DC circuit every time the starter is energized. Use the third set of contacts to de-energize a light in the DC circuit every time the starter is energized. Mark each terminal number used from the latching relay on the line diagram.

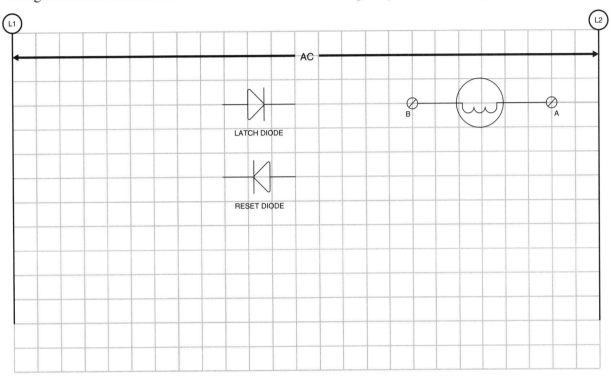

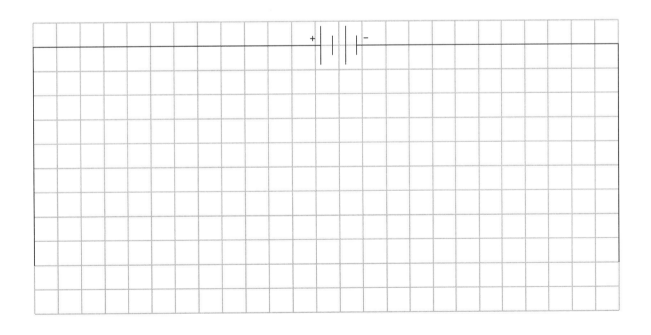

Sensing Devices and Controls

Tech-Chek 15

Name _____   Date _____

Electrical Motor Controls

_____   1. A(n) ___ photoelectric control is a photoelectric control that energizes the output switch when the target is missing (removed from the path of the beam).
A. light-operated   C. ON
B. dark-operated   D. OFF

_____   2. A(n) ___ photoelectric control is a photoelectric control that energizes the output switch when a target is present (breaks the path of the beam).
A. light-operated   C. ON
B. dark-operated   D. OFF

_____   3. The operating point at which the level of light intensity triggers the output is determined by the ___ adjustment.
A. sensitivity   C. voltage
B. differential   D. current

_____   4. ___ scan is a scanning technique which uses a special lens to filter the emitter's beam of light so that it is projected in one plane only.
A. Direct   C. Polarized
B. Retroreflective   D. Diffuse

_____   5. ___ scan is a scanning technique normally used in high-vibration applications.
A. Direct   C. Specular
B. Retroreflective   D. Convergent beam

_____   6. ___ scan is a scanning technique which should generally be the first choice for scanning targets that block most of the light beam.
A. Direct   C. Specular
B. Polarized   D. Convergent beam

_____   7. ___ scan is a scanning technique which is generally used in color mark detection.
A. Retroreflective   C. Specular
B. Polarized   D. Diffuse

_____   8. ___ scan is a scanning technique which places the transmitter and receiver at equal angles from a highly reflective surface.
A. Direct   C. Specular
B. Retroreflective   D. Diffuse

_____   9. ___ scan is a scanning technique which focuses the light beam to a fixed focal point in front of the photoreceiver.
A. Polarized   C. Diffuse
B. Specular   D. Convergent beam

_____ **10.** A(n) ___ sensor is a proximity switch that detects the proximity of a magnetic field.
    A. inductive   C. Hall effect
    B. capacitive   D. pendulum

_____ **11.** A(n) ___ proximity sensor is a proximity switch that detects conductive substances only.
    A. inductive   C. Hall effect
    B. capacitive   D. pendulum

_____ **12.** A(n) ___ sensor is a proximity switch that detects either conductive or nonconductive substances.
    A. inductive   C. Hall effect
    B. capacitive   D. pendulum

_____ **13.** Capacitive sensors work based on the ___ of the material to be sensed.

_____ **14.** ___ actuation is an active method of sensor activation in which a magnet is moved across the face of a Hall effect sensor at a constant distance (gap).

_____ **15.** In vane actuation, a(n) ___ shunts or redirects the ___ in the air gap away from the Hall effect sensor.

_____ **16.** A(n) ___ is a sensor that detects the movement (flow) of a liquid or gas using a solid-state device.

_____ **17.** The amount of current drawn by a load when energized is known as ___.
    A. operating current   C. direct current
    B. minimum holding current   D. load current

_____ **18.** ___ is the minimum amount of current required to keep a sensor operating.

_____ **19.** ___ is any object other than the object to be detected that is sensed by a sensor.

_____ **20.** A distance of ___ is required within or next to a material that may be detected when using non-flush-mounted inductive and capacitive proximity sensors.

Scanning Methods

_____ **1.** Direct scan

_____ **2.** Retroreflective scan

_____ **3.** Polarized scan

_____ **4.** Specular scan

_____ **5.** Diffuse scan

Sensing Devices and Controls

Name _____ Date _____

Level Control

Use Data Sheet J on page 269 to complete the line diagram. Use standard lettering, numbering, and coding information. Mark all manufacturers' numbers (1-11) on the line diagram.

1. Design a circuit that uses two light source/photo-receiver pairs to keep a hopper fill level between a high and a low limit. The top source/photoreceiver pair turns a pump motor starter OFF, and the bottom source/photoreceiver pair turns the pump motor starter ON.

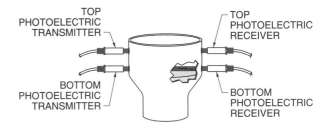

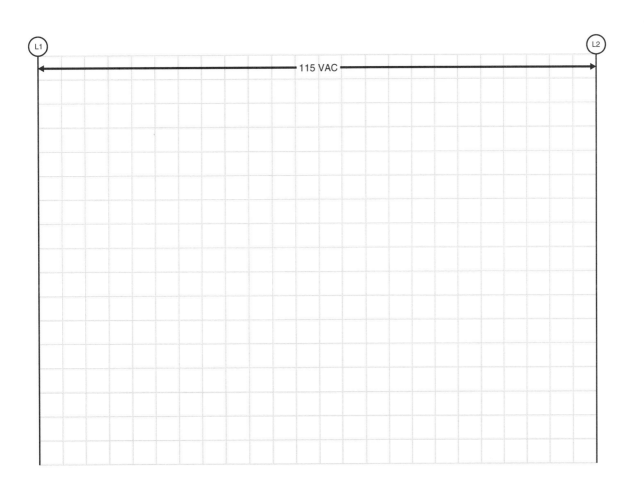

Sensing Devices and Controls

Worksheet 15-2

Name _____ Date _____

Part Checking

Use Data Sheet J on page 269 to complete the line diagram. Use standard lettering, numbering, and coding information. Mark all manufacturers' numbers (1-11) on the line diagram. Assume there is no space between the cans.

1. Design a circuit so that dark caps are checked for white liners by a photoelectric scanner. The scanner activates a solenoid valve that controls a cylinder that rejects caps that lack liners. The solenoid is activated 5 sec after the scanner sees a cap without a liner. The white liners act to stop the reflection from the tin bottom. The tin bottom acts as a reflector.

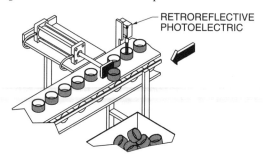

RETROREFLECTIVE PHOTOELECTRIC

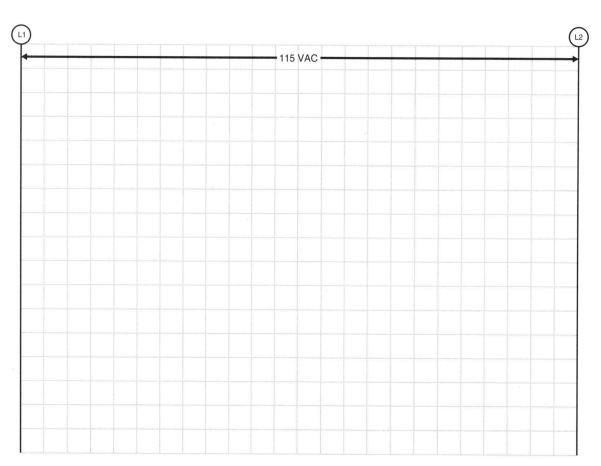

L1 — 115 VAC — L2

Sensing Devices and Controls

Worksheet 15-3

Name _____ Date _____

Carton Filling

Use Data Sheet J on page 269 to complete the line diagram. Use standard lettering, numbering, and coding information. Mark all manufacturers' numbers (1-11) on the line diagram. Label each timer as to its time setting.

1. Design a photoelectric control that stops a conveyor motor and fills a carton. The photoelectric control does not stop the motor until 2 sec (Timer 1) after it sees the carton. The fill process is controlled by a timer that controls a fill solenoid for a preset time duration. It takes 15 sec (Timer 2) to fill the carton. After the carton is filled, the fill solenoid is turned OFF, the conveyor motor is turned ON, and the timer is reset.

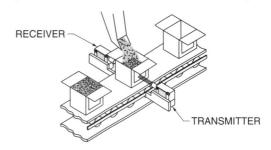

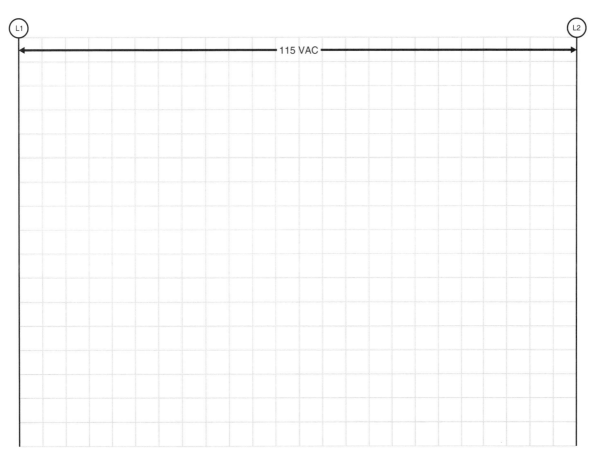

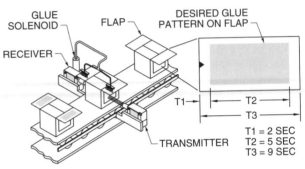

Sensing Devices and Controls

Worksheet 15-4

Name _____ Date _____

Carton Gluing

Use Data Sheet J on page 269 to complete the line diagram. Use standard lettering, numbering, and coding information. Mark all manufacturers' numbers (1-11) on the line diagram. Label each timer as to its time setting.

1. Design a photoelectric control circuit that turns ON a glue nozzle when a carton passes. The glue nozzle is controlled by a solenoid valve. The conveyor motor is ON at all times. Do not show the conveyor circuit in the line diagram. The glue operation does not start until 2 sec (Timer 1) after the photoelectric control sees the carton. The glue operation stops after 5 sec (Timer 2), even though the carton takes 9 sec to pass the photoelectric control. This prevents glue from being sprayed on the conveyor belt.

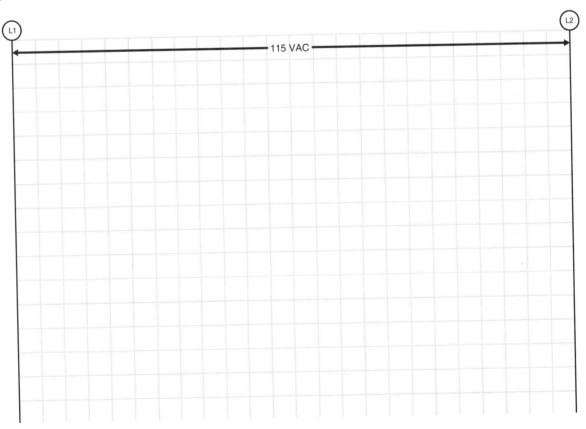

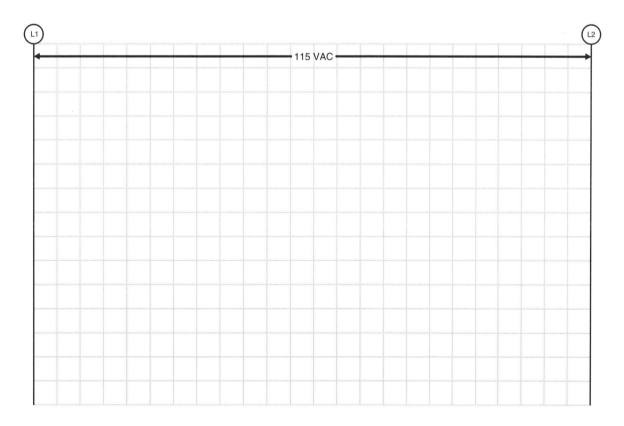

Name _____ Date _____

Conveyor Jam Control

Use Data Sheet J on page 269 to complete the line diagram. Use standard lettering, numbering, and coding information. Mark all manufacturers' numbers (1-11) on the line diagram.

1. Design a photoelectric control circuit that sounds an alarm if there is a jam or if there are no products moving along a conveyor system. Normally spaced products move past the photoelectric control (set for dark-operated) every 1 sec to 3 sec. The circuit sounds the alarm if no product has moved past the control in 9 sec (use an ON-delay timer set for 9 sec), or if a product stays in front of the control for more than 6 sec (use an ON-delay timer set for 6 sec). Mark the 6 sec timer TR1 and the 9 sec timer TR2.

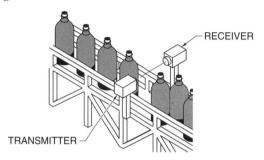

L1 ———————————— 115 VAC ———————————— L2

Sensing Devices and Controls

Worksheet 15-6

Name _____ Date _____

Paper Roll Monitoring

Use Data Sheet J on page 269 to complete the line diagram. Use standard lettering, numbering, and coding information. Mark all manufacturers' numbers (1-11) on the line diagram.

1. Design a circuit in which the position of a photoelectric control (set for light-operated) monitors the diameter of a roll of paper. The control should turn OFF a drive motor and sound an alarm when the roll of paper is almost empty. Include a standard start/stop pushbutton station to start the drive motor and stop it manually if required.

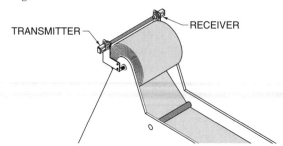

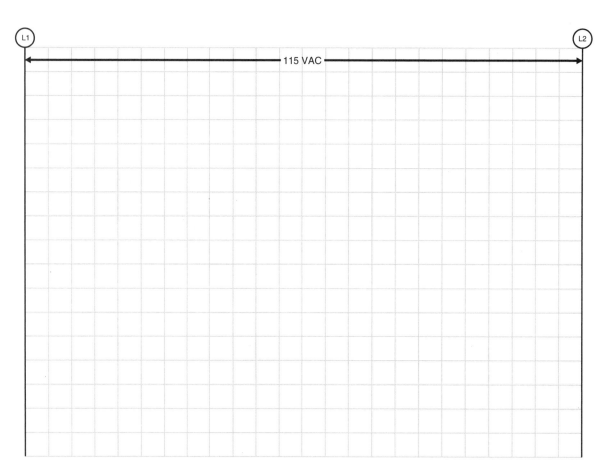

Sensing Devices and Controls

Worksheet 15-7

Name _____ Date _____

Steel Cutting Operation

Use Data Sheet K on page 270 to complete the line diagram. Use standard lettering, numbering, and coding information. Mark all manufacturers' numbers (1-11) on the line diagram.

1. Design a circuit with a proximity switch that is used to automatically stop a motor from supplying steel to a cutting press. A start pushbutton is used to start the steel infeed, and a proximity switch or stop pushbutton is used to stop the steel infeed.

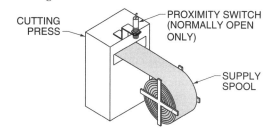

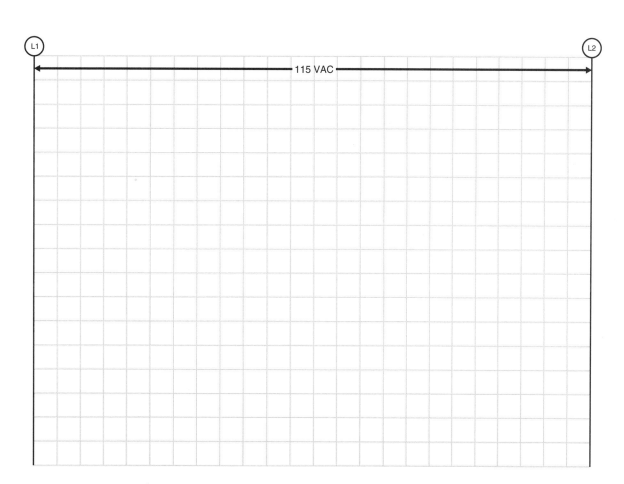

Sensing Devices and Controls

Worksheet 15-8

Name _____ Date _____

Bottle Cap Control

Use Data Sheet J on page 269 and Data Sheet K on page 270 to complete the line diagram. Use standard lettering, numbering, and coding information. Mark all manufacturers' numbers (1-11) on the line diagram.

1. Design a circuit in which an alarm sounds if a bottle cap is missing. The photoelectric control (set for dark-operated) is used to detect if a bottle is present. The proximity control detects if there is a cap on the bottle. Show both the photoelectric and proximity controls in the circuit.

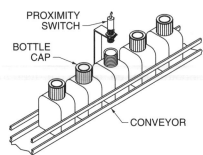

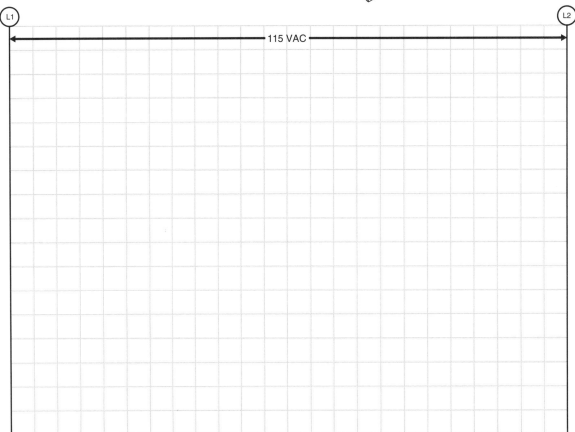

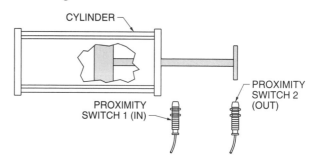

Sensing Devices and Controls

Worksheet 15-9

Name _____ Date _____

Piston Control

Use Data Sheet K on page 270 to complete the line diagram. Use standard lettering, numbering, and coding information. Mark all manufacturers' numbers (1-11) on the line diagram.

1. Design a circuit in which two proximity switches are used to cycle the piston in a cylinder back and forth automatically. A standard start/stop pushbutton station with memory is used to start and stop the automatic cycling. The piston is controlled by a double-solenoid fluid power valve. One solenoid controls the piston out function and the other controls the piston in function. Power must be maintained on the solenoids to keep the piston moving.

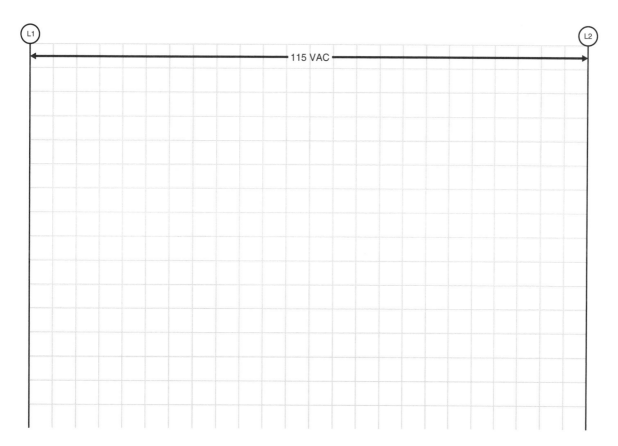

Sensing Devices and Controls

Worksheet 15-10

Name _____ Date _____

Proximity Switch Piston Control

Use Data Sheet L on page 271 to complete the line diagram. Use standard lettering, numbering, and coding information. Mark all manufacturers' numbers (1-11) on the line diagram.

1. Design a circuit in which two proximity switches are used to cycle the piston in a cylinder back and forth automatically. A standard start/stop pushbutton station with memory is used to start and stop the automatic cycling. The piston is controlled by a double-solenoid fluid power valve. One solenoid controls the piston out function and the other controls the piston in function. Power must be maintained on the solenoids to keep the piston moving.

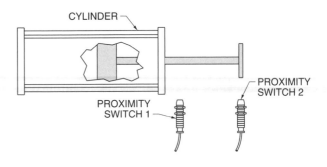

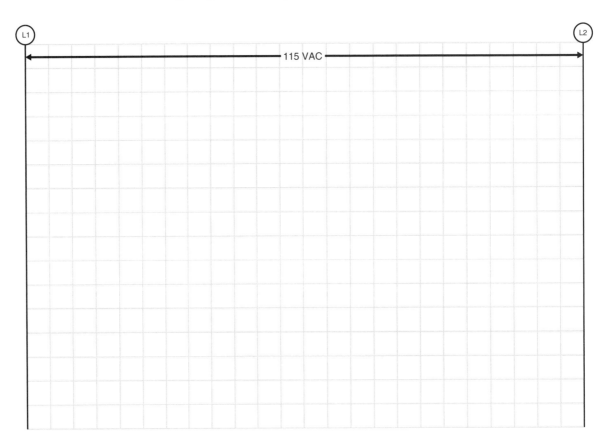

Sensing Devices and Controls

Worksheet 15-11

Name _____   Date _____

Product Jam-Up Detection

Photoelectric sensors may be used to detect possible product jam-ups.

1. Design the control circuit using a photoelectric sensor. Use a standard start/stop pushbutton station to control the conveyor motor. If the photoelectric sensor is blocked by a product jam-up for more than 5 sec, the conveyor stops and an alarm will sound. Mark each wire number used from the photoelectric sensor.

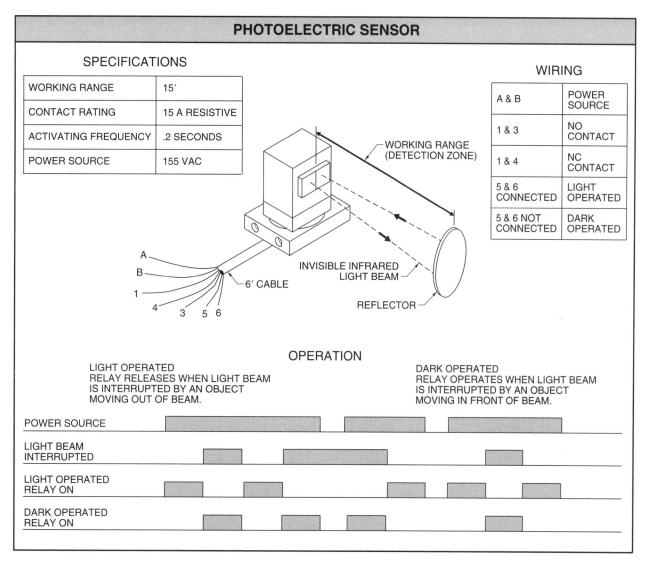

PHOTOELECTRIC SENSOR

SPECIFICATIONS

WORKING RANGE	15′
CONTACT RATING	15 A RESISTIVE
ACTIVATING FREQUENCY	.2 SECONDS
POWER SOURCE	155 VAC

WIRING

A & B	POWER SOURCE
1 & 3	NO CONTACT
1 & 4	NC CONTACT
5 & 6 CONNECTED	LIGHT OPERATED
5 & 6 NOT CONNECTED	DARK OPERATED

WORKING RANGE (DETECTION ZONE)

INVISIBLE INFRARED LIGHT BEAM

REFLECTOR

6′ CABLE

A
B
1
4
3 5 6

OPERATION

LIGHT OPERATED
RELAY RELEASES WHEN LIGHT BEAM
IS INTERRUPTED BY AN OBJECT
MOVING OUT OF BEAM.

DARK OPERATED
RELAY OPERATES WHEN LIGHT BEAM
IS INTERRUPTED BY AN OBJECT
MOVING IN FRONT OF BEAM.

POWER SOURCE

LIGHT BEAM INTERRUPTED

LIGHT OPERATED RELAY ON

DARK OPERATED RELAY ON

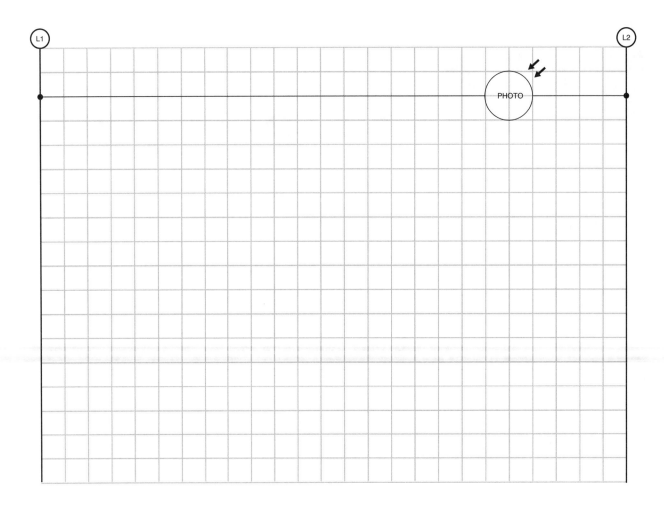

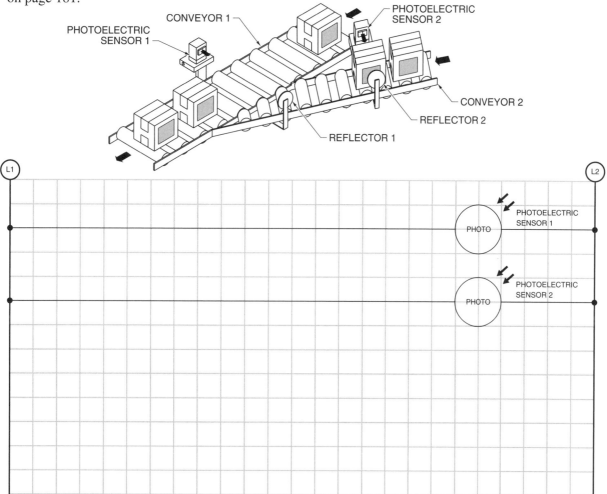

Sensing Devices
and Controls

Worksheet 15-12

Name _____ Date _____

Conveyor Merging Control

Two photoelectric sensors may be used to control the merging of two conveyors.

1. Design the control circuit using two photoelectric sensors. Use a standard start/stop pushbutton station to control Conveyor 1. Conveyor 2 runs when Conveyor 1 is running and when two boxes are not merging simultaneously. Design the circuit so both conveyor motors operate if no box is detected. If Photoelectric Sensor 1 detects a box and Photoelectric Sensor 2 does not, both conveyors continue to run. If Photoelectric Sensors 1 and 2 both detect a box, Conveyor 1 continues to run, and Conveyor 2 stops until Conveyor 1 is clear. Mark each wire number used from each photoelectric sensor. Use the photoelectric sensor diagram on page 181.

Sensing Devices and Controls

Name _____ Date _____

Bottle Detection

Four capacitive proximity sensors may be used to detect bottles through a carton. Capacitive proximity sensors can detect plastic, glass, or metal containers inside the carton.

1. Design the control circuit using four capacitive proximity sensors and four DC-to-AC solid-state relays. In the DC circuit, each capacitive proximity sensor energizes one light and one solid-state relay when a bottle is present. In the AC circuit, the four solid-state relay contacts energize an operate delay relay. The relay is set for 5 sec and controls the conveyor motor starter. When all four sensors detect a bottle, the conveyor motor runs for 5 sec and automatically advances each carton after it is filled. If the conveyor does not advance, an operator checks the lights to see which bottles have not dropped. If the carton advances, the circuit is automatically reset when the carton passes the four sensors. Mark the color of each wire used on the sensor.

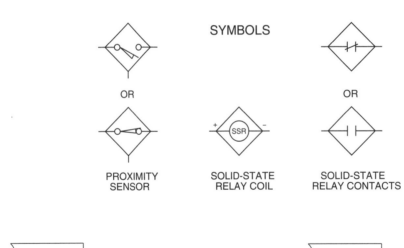

SYMBOLS

OR · OR

PROXIMITY
SENSOR

SOLID-STATE
RELAY COIL

SOLID-STATE
RELAY CONTACTS

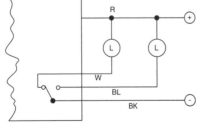

NPN TRANSISTOR OUTPUT
(CURRENT SINK)

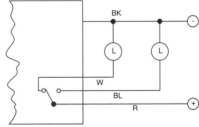

PNP TRANSISTOR OUTPUT
(CURRENT SOURCE)

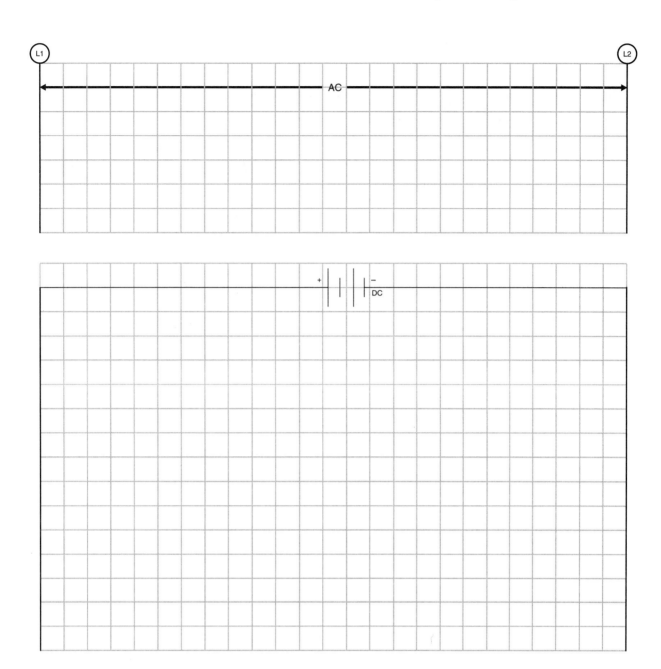

Sensing Devices and Controls

Worksheet 15-14

Name _____ Date _____

Drilling Operation Control

A drill motor may be used to drill a hole in a workpiece. Proximity Sensor 1 detects the presence of the workpiece. Proximity Sensor 2 automatically returns the drill. The movement of the drill motor is controlled by a hydraulic valve. The valve is controlled by two solenoids.

1. Draw the control circuit using two sensors and two DC-to-AC solid-state relays. In the DC circuit, each sensor controls a solid-state relay. In the AC circuit, a pushbutton energizes the advance solenoid if the workpiece is in place. The other sensor automatically returns the drill motor. Mark the color of each wire used on the proximity sensor.

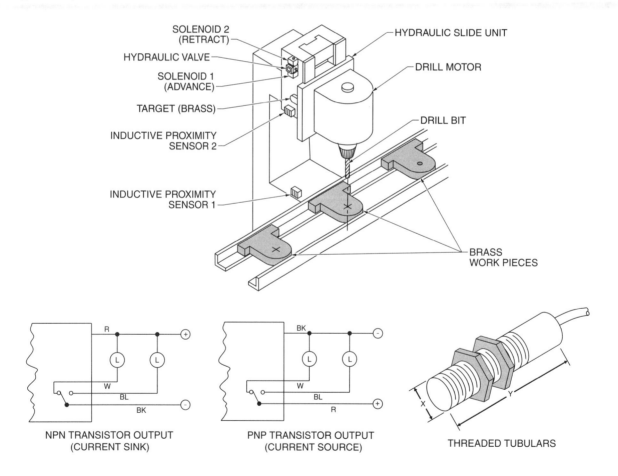

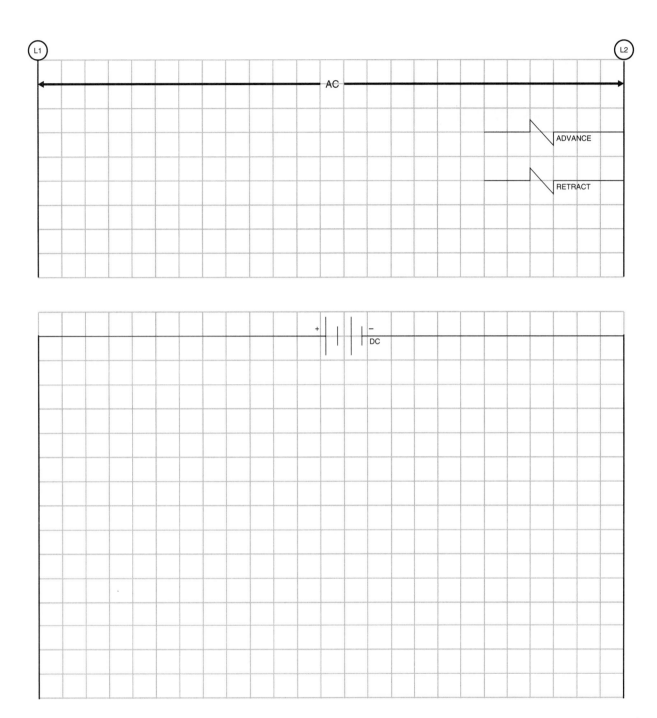

Sensing Devices and Controls

Name _____ Date _____

Glass Panel Detection

A capacitive proximity sensor may be used to detect the presence of glass panels moving along a production line.

1. Draw the control circuit using a capacitive proximity sensor and two DC-to-AC solid-state relays. In the DC circuit, the proximity sensor energizes two solid-state relays when the glass panels are present. In the AC circuit, a three-position selector switch controls a two-speed conveyor motor that moves the glass panels along the production line. When the selector switch is in the low position, the low-speed starter is energized. When the low-speed starter is energized, glass panels move along the production line at 15 sec intervals. When the selector switch is in the high position, the high-speed starter is energized. When the high-speed starter is energized, glass panels move along the production line at 10 sec intervals. When the selector switch is in the OFF position, no starter is energized. Design the circuit so an alarm sounds when the proximity sensor does not detect a glass panel every 15 sec in low speed. An alarm also sounds when the proximity sensor does not detect a glass panel every 10 sec in high Use NPN Transistor Output and PNP Transistor Output diagrams on page 186. Mark the color of each wire used on the proximity sensor.

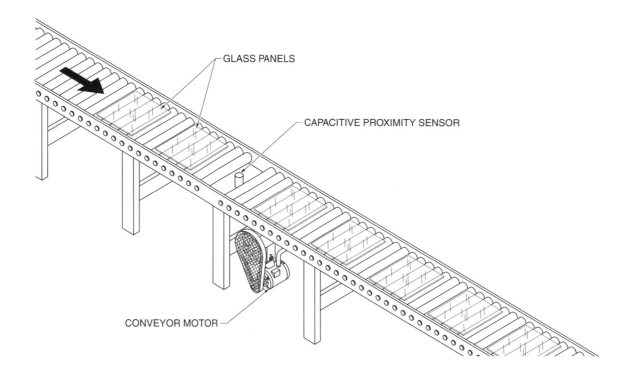

GLASS PANELS

CAPACITIVE PROXIMITY SENSOR

CONVEYOR MOTOR

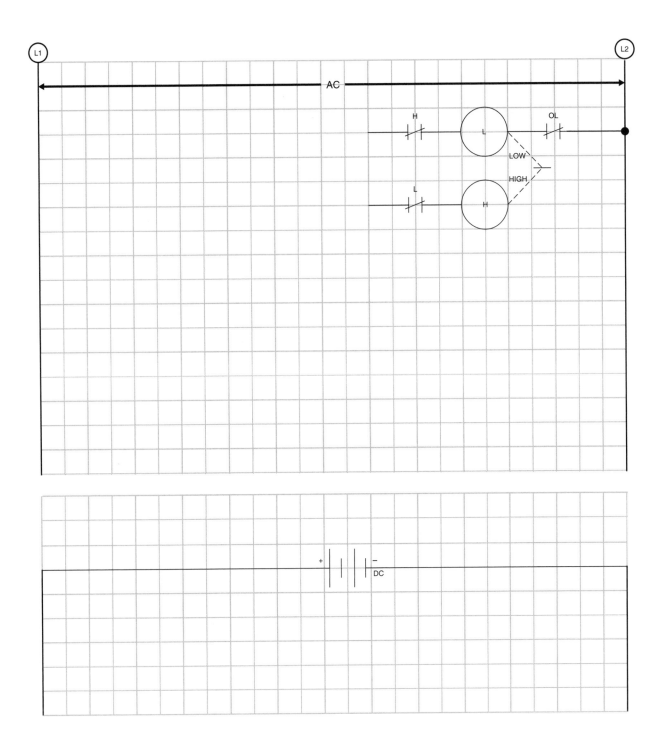

Programmable Controllers

Tech-Chek 16

Name _____   Date _____

Electrical Motor Controls

_____ 1. ___ manufacturing produces such goods as automobiles and refrigerators.
   A. Movable   C. Process
   B. Multiple   D. Discrete parts

_____ 2. ___ manufacturing produces such goods as food and gas.
   A. Movable   C. Process
   B. Multiple   D. Discrete parts

_____ 3. The ___ section of a PLC organizes all system control activities.
   A. power supply   C. processor
   B. input/output   D. programming

_____ 4. The ___ section of a PLC allows inputs into the PLC through a keyboard.

_____ 5. The ___ section of a PLC provides the voltage required for internal operation and charging the internal battery.

_____ 6. The ___ section of a PLC functions as the eyes, ears, and hands of the PLC.
   A. power supply   C. processor
   B. input/output   D. programming

_____ 7. The ___ mode is used to execute the program in a PLC.
   A. program   C. test
   B. run   D. fast

_____ 8. The ___ mode is used when developing the logic of a circuit.
   A. program   C. test
   B. run   D. fast

_____ 9. The ___ mode is used when forcing inputs and outputs.
   A. program   C. test
   B. run   D. fast

_____ 10. A ___ system has multiple transmitters and receivers connected to a single-wire pair.
   A. hardwired   C. hand-operated
   B. self-diagnosis   D. multiplexing

_____ 11. In a PLC line diagram, the horizontal lines are known as ___.

_____ **12.** A(n) ___ operation is an operation that has feedback from the output to the input.

_____ **13.** Two types of higher-level PLC languages are ___ and ___.
    A. Functional Blocks; English   C. Line Diagrams;
       Statement   English Statement
    B. Boolean; Functional Blocks   D. Boolean; English Statement

_____ **14.** A(n) ___ is one execution cycle of a PLC line diagram.

_____ **15.** A(n) ___ diagram is a line diagram that better matches the PLC's language.

_____ **16.** The PLC battery should be replaced as recommended by the manufacturer or ___.

_____ **17.** The disable command is opposite of the ___ command.

_____ **18.** A(n) ___ circuit is used to suppress a voltage spike.

_____ **19.** HMI stands for ___.
    A. heavy manufacturing industry   C. human machine interface
    B. horizontally maintained   D. heavy metal interference
       interface

_____ **20.** One main advantage of using a PLC is that the PLC eliminates the need for ___ on motor starters, external relays, external timers, and counters.

_____ **21.** A(n) ___ is a group of data values that are displayed as a group and whose status may be monitored.

PLC Logic Functions

_____ **1.** AND logic

_____ **2.** OR logic

_____ **3.** NOT logic

_____ **4.** NAND logic

_____ **5.** NOR logic

(A)

(B)

(C)

(D)

(E)

PLC Programming Diagrams

1. Redraw the standard line diagram as a basic PLC programming diagram.

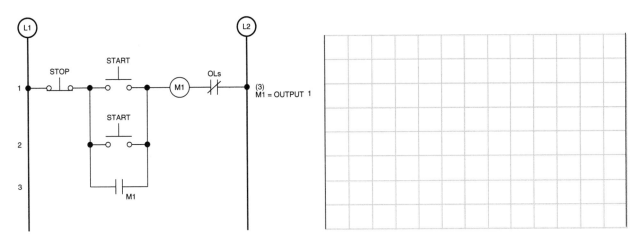

2. Redraw the basic PLC programming diagram as a standard line diagram.

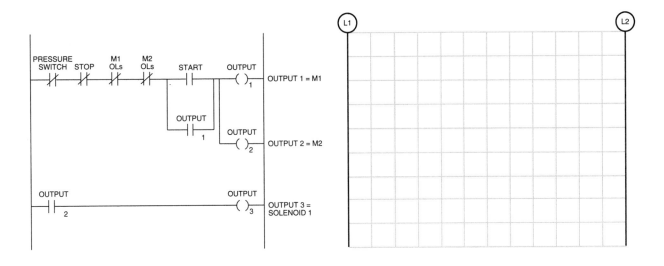

Programmable Controllers

Worksheet 16-1

Name _____ Date _____

Line Diagram to PLC Diagram Conversion
Use the Device Equivalents table to complete the PLC programming diagram.

1. Draw the basic PLC programming diagram of the standard line diagram.

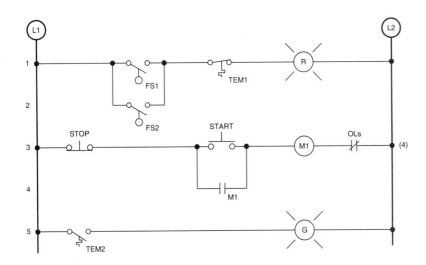

DEVICE EQUIVALENTS
FS1 = INPUT 1
FS2 = INPUT 2
TEM1 = INPUT 3
TEM2 = INPUT 4
STOP = INPUT 5
START = INPUT 6
OLs = INPUT 7
RED LAMP = INPUT 8
GREEN LAMP = INPUT 9
STARTER 1 = INPUT 10

Programmable Controllers

Worksheet 16-2

Name _____   Date _____

Selector Switch Line Diagram to PLC Diagram Conversion

Use the Device Equivalents table to complete the PLC programming diagram.

1. Draw the basic PLC programming diagram of the standard line diagram.

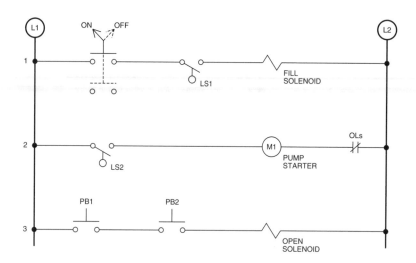

DEVICE EQUIVALENTS
SELECTOR SWITCH = INPUT 1
LEVEL SWITCH 1 = INPUT 2
LEVEL SWITCH 2 = INPUT 3
PUSHBUTTON 1 = INPUT 4
PUSHBUTTON 2 = INPUT 5
OLs = INPUT 6
FILL SOLENOID = OUTPUT 1
OPEN SOLENOID = OUTPUT 2
PUMP STARTER = OUTPUT 3

Programmable Controllers

Worksheet 16-3

Name _____   Date _____

Two-Speed Line Diagram to PLC Diagram Conversion

Use the Device Equivalents table to complete the PLC programming diagram.

1. Draw the basic PLC programming diagram of the standard line diagram.

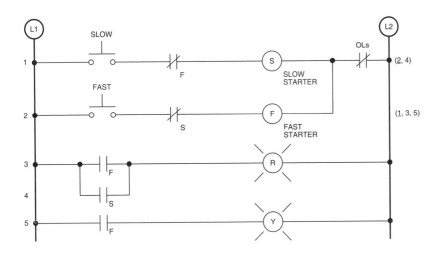

DEVICE EQUIVALENTS		
SLOW PUSHBUTTON	=	INPUT 1
FAST PUSHBUTTON	=	INPUT 2
OLs	=	INPUT 3
SLOW COIL	=	OUTPUT 1
FAST COIL	=	OUTPUT 2
RED LAMP	=	OUTPUT 3
YELLOW LAMP	=	OUTPUT 4

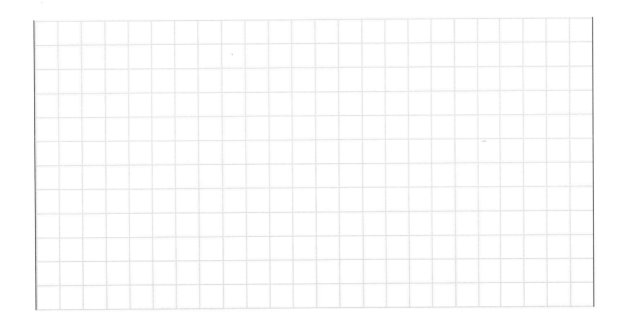

Programmable Controllers

Worksheet 16-4

Name _____   Date _____

Forward and Reversing Line Diagram to PLC Diagram Conversion
Use the Device Equivalents table to complete the PLC programming diagram.

1. Draw the basic PLC programming diagram of the standard line diagram.

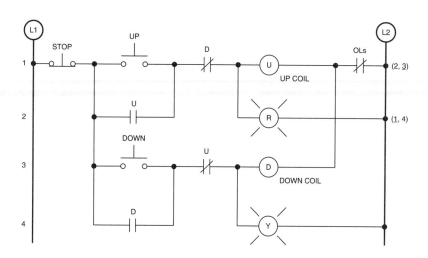

DEVICE EQUIVALENTS	
STOP PUSHBUTTON	= INPUT 1
UP PUSHBUTTON	= INPUT 2
DOWN PUSHBUTTON	= INPUT 3
OLs	= INPUT 4
UP COIL	= OUTPUT 1
DOWN COIL	= OUTPUT 2
RED LAMP	= OUTPUT 3
YELLOW LAMP	= OUTPUT 4

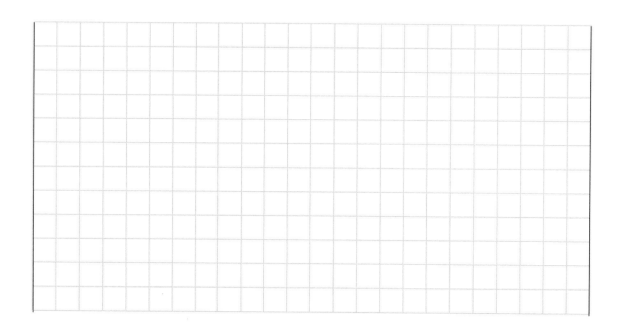

![Programmable Controllers — Worksheet 16-5]

Name _____   Date _____

Forward and Reversing PLC Diagram to Line Diagram Conversion

Use the Device Equivalents table to complete the standard line diagram.

1. Draw the standard line diagram of the basic PLC programming diagram.

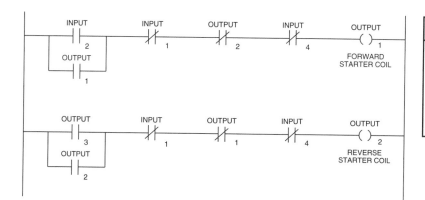

DEVICE EQUIVALENTS		
INPUT 1 = START PUSHBUTTON		
INPUT 2 = FORWARD PUSHBUTTON		
INPUT 3 = REVERSE PUSHBUTTON		
INPUT 4 = OLs		
OUTPUT 1 = FORWARD STARTER COIL		
OUTPUT 2 = REVERSE STARTER COIL		

Programmable Controllers

Worksheet 16-6

Name _____ Date _____

Two-Speed PLC Diagram to Line Diagram Conversion

Use the Device Equivalents table to complete the standard line diagram.

1. Draw the standard line diagram of the basic PLC programming diagram.

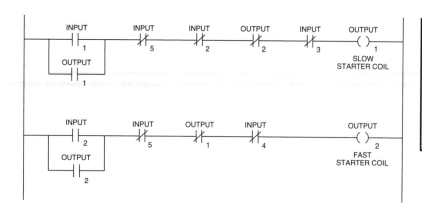

DEVICE EQUIVALENTS
INPUT 1 = SLOW PUSHBUTTON
INPUT 2 = FAST PUSHBUTTON
INPUT 3 = OLs (SLOW STARTER)
INPUT 4 = OLs (FAST STARTER)
INPUT 5 = STOP PUSHBUTTON
OUTPUT 1 = SLOW STARTER COIL
OUTPUT 2 = FAST STARTER COIL

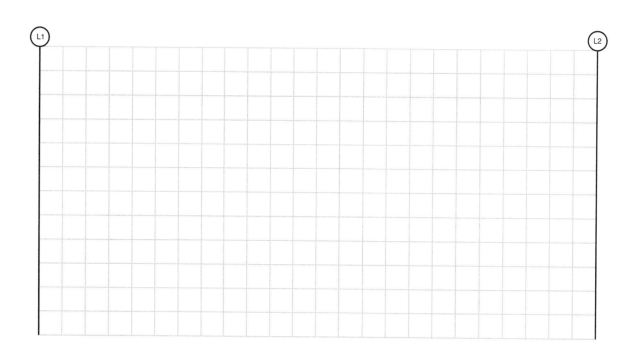

Programmable Controllers

Worksheet 16-7

Name _____   Date _____

System Input and Output Identification

1. Identify the type (input or output), name (limit switch or temperature switch), and function (starts scalper motor) of the inputs and outputs for the motor control circuit.

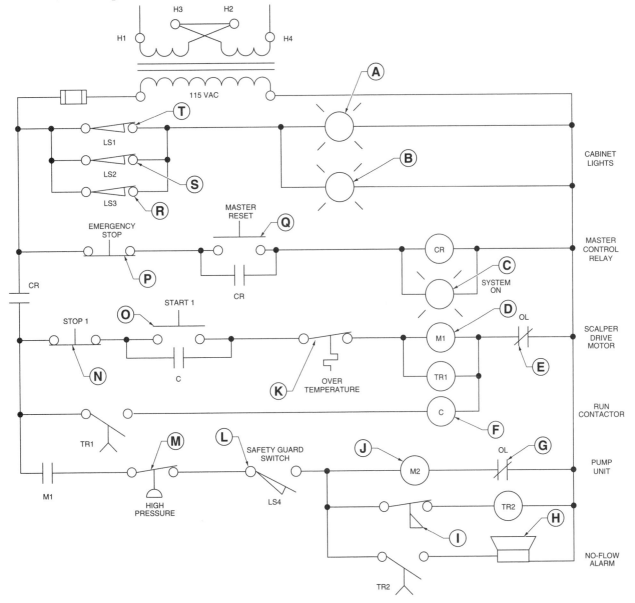

	Type	Name	Function
	MOTOR CONTROL CIRCUIT		
	Type	**Name**	**Function**
A	Output	Light	Light cabinet interior
B			
C			
D			
E			
F			
G			
H			
I			
J			
K			
L			
M			
N			
O			
P			
Q			
R			
S			
T			

Programmable Controllers

Worksheet 16-8

Name _____ Date _____

System Input and Output Connections

1. Connect the inputs to the input modules in the order in which they are listed on page 202. Mark any extras as spares.

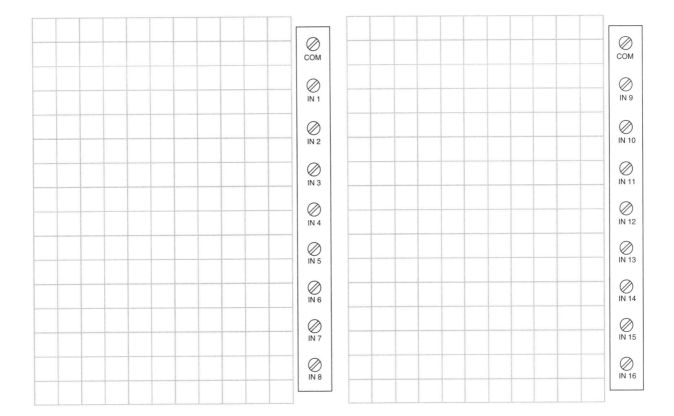

2. Connect the outputs to the output module in the order in which they are listed on page 202. Mark any extras as spares.

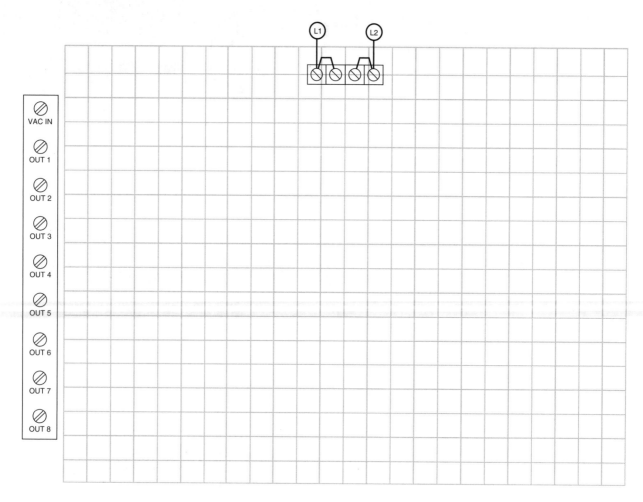

Programmable Controllers

Name _____ Date _____

Alarm Output Connection

Nuisance tripping can occur when the alarm contacts on a programmable controller close for only a few seconds. To prevent nuisance tripping, a timer is added to the circuit to delay the activation of the alarm.

1. Draw the line diagram of the programmable controller alarm, adding an operate delay relay to prevent the alarm from tripping unless the alarm contacts are closed for more than 3 sec.

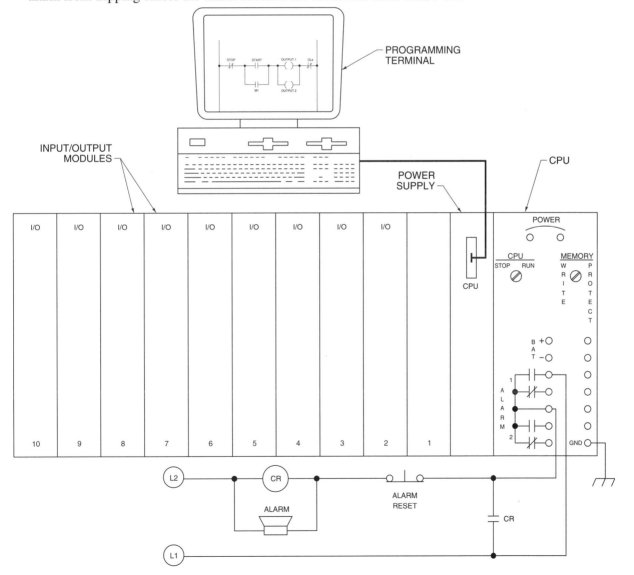

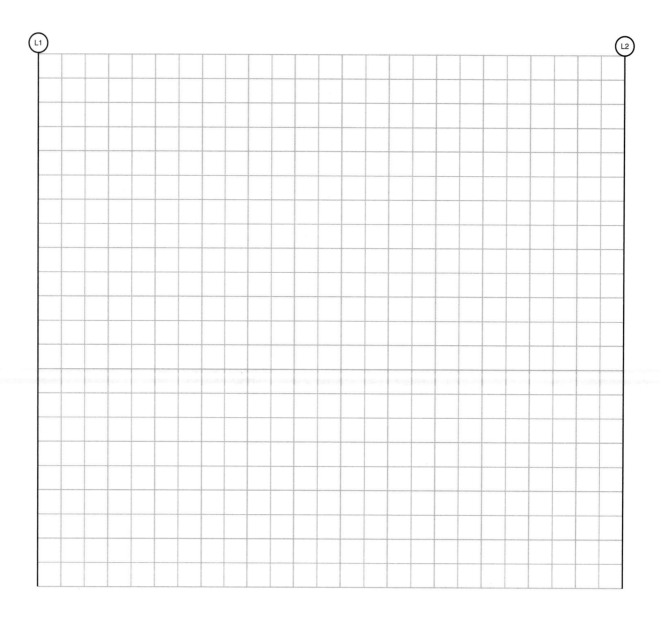

Reduced-Voltage Starting

Tech-Chek 17

Name _____ Date _____

Electrical Motor Controls

_____ 1. Reduced-voltage starting is used to ___.
  A. reduce large current C. control full-voltage starting
  B. control speed D. start difficult loads

_____ 2. Sudden high torque is known as ___.

_____ 3. A drop in voltage of more than 10% (but not to 0 V) below the normal rated line voltage lasting from 0.5 cycles up to 1 minute is known as ___.
  A. voltage draw C. voltage sag
  B. reduced voltage D. full-load current

_____ 4. The purpose of a rheostat is to ___.

_____ 5. A DC motor, unlike an AC motor, may need reduced-voltage starting to ___.
  A. reduce starting current C. protect the electrical environment
  B. reduce starting torque D. prevent motor damage

_____ 6. ___ starting uses a tapped three-phase transformer to provide reduced-voltage starting.

_____ 7. Current and ___ of a motor are reduced when voltage to the motor is reduced.

_____ 8. Reduced voltage is applied to 3ϕ motors because 1ϕ motors are typically ___.

_____ 9. ___ current is the current required by a motor to produce full-load torque at the motor's rated speed.

_____ 10. ___ is the steady-state current taken from the power lines when the voltage is applied and the rotor locked.

_____ 11. The five methods used in reduced-voltage starting are resistive, part-winding, wye-to-delta, solid-state, and ___.

_____ 12. Two reduced-voltage starting methods that are not adjustable to more than two steps without additional circuitry are the wye-to-delta and ___ starting methods.

_____ 13. The reduced-voltage starting method which is adjustable through its entire range is the ___ starting method.

_____ 14. ___ current is the maximum current permitted by the utility company in any one step of an increment start.

_____ 15. A(n) ___ motor has two sets of identical windings which are intended to be used in parallel.

_____ **16.** Starting current for motors is ___ times the full-load current.

_____ **17.** A(n) ___ is two antiparallel thyristors and a triac mounted on the same chip.

_____ **18.** A(n) ___ is used to convert electrical energy into a rotating mechanical force.

_____ **19.** ___ starting uses a resistor connected in each motor line (in one line in a single-phase starter) to produce a voltage drop.

_____ **20.** ___ starting is a method of starting a motor by first applying power to part of the motor's coil windings for starting and then applying power to the remaining coil windings for normal running.

_____ **21.** ___ starting uses SCRs to control motor voltage, current, and torque during acceleration.

_____ **22.** ___ starting provides the highest possible starting torque per ampere of line current.

_____ **23.** The starting current of a DC motor with an armature resistance of 1 Ω connected to a 208 V supply is ___.

_____ **24.** As a DC motor accelerates, a(n) ___ is generated which reduces the current in the motor.

_____ **25.** The running current of a DC motor with an armature resistance of 1 Ω that is connected to a 230 V supply and generating 200 V of EMF is ___.

_____ **26.** ___ are used to switch low-level DC only.

_____ **27.** ___ are used as solid-state low- and high-level DC switches.

_____ **28.** Two ___ can be mounted in an antiparallel configuration to switch AC.

_____ **29.** A(n) ___ starter is a device that provides a gradual voltage increase (ramp up) during AC motor starting.

_____ **30.** A(n) ___ is a three-terminal semiconductor that is used as an AC switch.

Reduced-Voltage Starting

Worksheet 17-1

Name _____ Date _____

Primary Resistor Starting

Complete the wiring diagram according to the line diagram. Do not make any wire splices or additional terminal connections on the wiring diagram. All connections must run from terminal screw to terminal screw.

1. Design a circuit so that when the start pushbutton is pressed, the contactor (M) and the time delay relay (TR) are energized and the motor is connected to the incoming power lines through the resistor bank. After the time delay relay has timed out, the timed closed contacts close and contactor A1 is energized, shorting across each of the three resistors in the resistor bank. This automatically switches the motor to full power.

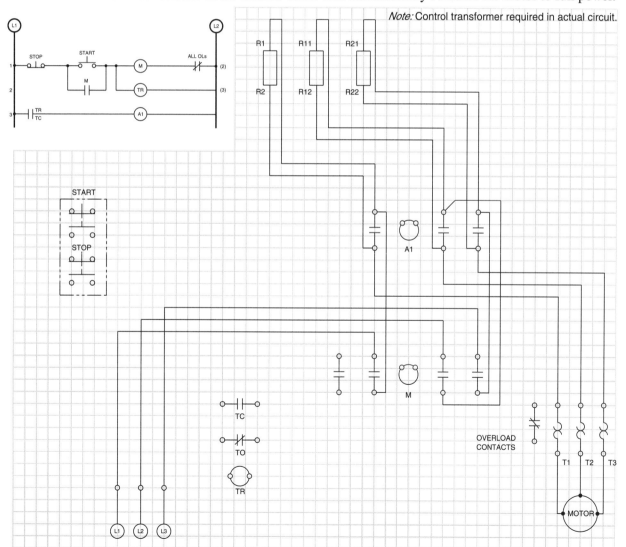

Reduced-Voltage Starting

Worksheet 17-2

Name _____ Date _____

Part-Winding Starting

Complete the circuits based on the information given. Do not make any wire splices or additional terminal connections on the wiring diagram. All connections must run from terminal screw to terminal screw.

1. Design a circuit so that when the start pushbutton is pressed, contactor M1 is energized first and power is applied to motor terminals T1, T2, and T3. After the time delay, the normally open auxiliary interlock on M1 times out, the timed-closed (TC) contacts close, and the M2 contactor is energized, connecting power to the second winding (motor terminals T7, T8, and T9). The motor is stopped by pressing the stop pushbutton, which drops out both contactors. If motor terminals T4, T5, and T6 are not internally connected, they should be wired together at the terminal box.

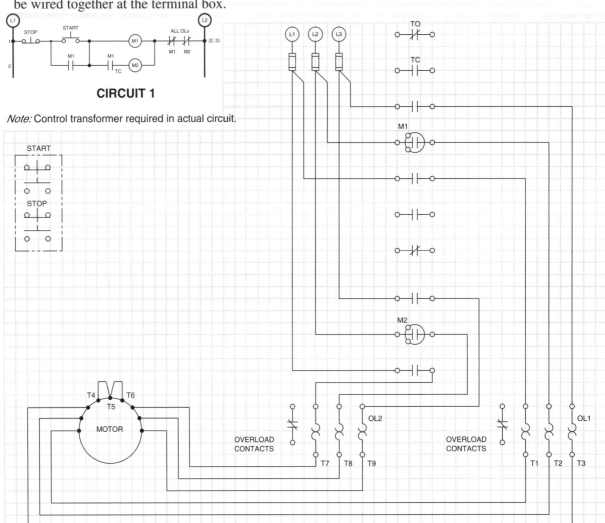

CIRCUIT 1

Note: Control transformer required in actual circuit.

2. Redraw the line diagram of Circuit 1, adding a separate timer to the circuit that is used when a time delay auxiliary contact is not used.

CIRCUIT 2

3. Redraw the line diagram of Circuit 1, adding a second timer that does not allow the motor to be restarted until it has stopped for 10 min. Replace the pushbutton station with a temperature controller because this type of operation is normally automatic.

4. Redraw Circuit 2, adding a cooling fan motor to run for 10 min after the reduced-voltage-starting motor has turned OFF.

Reduced-Voltage Starting

Worksheet 17-3

Name _____   Date _____

Wye/Delta Connections

Complete the wiring diagram according to the line diagram. Do not make any wire splices or additional terminal connections on the wiring diagram. All connections must run from terminal screw to terminal screw.

1. Design a circuit so that when the start pushbutton is pressed, contactors S and M1 are energized. Contactor S connects motor terminals T4, T5, and T6. Contactor M1 connects the incoming power lines to motor terminals T1, T2, and T3, causing the motor to start in a wye-connected configuration. After the time delay normally closed interlock on M1 times out, the timed-open (TO) contacts open, dropping out contactor S and picking up contactor M2. The M2 contactor applies power to terminals T4, T5, and T6, bringing the motor up to full speed in a delta-connected configuration. The motor is stopped by pressing the stop pushbutton, which drops out all three contactors.

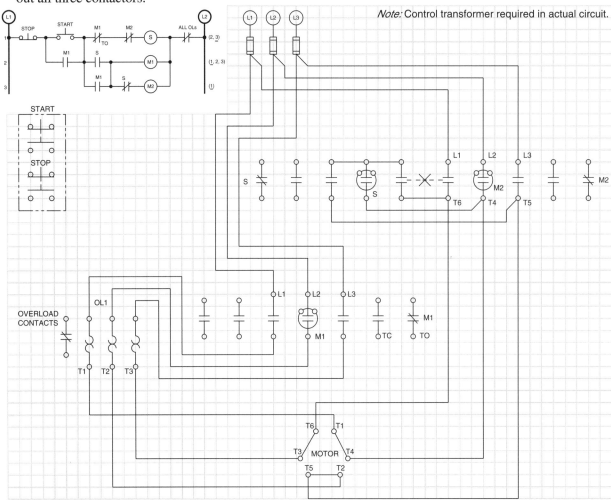

Note: Control transformer required in actual circuit.

Reduced-Voltage Starting

Worksheet 17-4

Name _____ Date _____

Autotransformer Starting

Complete the wiring diagram according to the line diagram. Do not make any wire splices or additional terminal connections on the wiring diagram. All connections must run from terminal screw to terminal screw.

1. Design a circuit so that when the start pushbutton is pressed, the time delay relay (TR) and contactors S and M are energized, applying power through the windings of the autotransformer to the motor. When the time delay relay times out, the timed-open (TO) contacts open and the timed-closed (TC) contacts close, the S contactor drops out, and the R contactor is energized, switching the motor to full-line voltage. The autotransformer incorporates a thermal protector switch embedded in the winding of each of the two transformer coils. These devices (TPA and TPB) sense the heat rise in the coils and open their normally closed contacts if the temperature limits are reached. This allows full current to the lockout relay (LR) and opens its normally closed contacts. LR is normally shorted out by the thermal protector switches. The lockout relay has to be hand reset to restore power to the line.

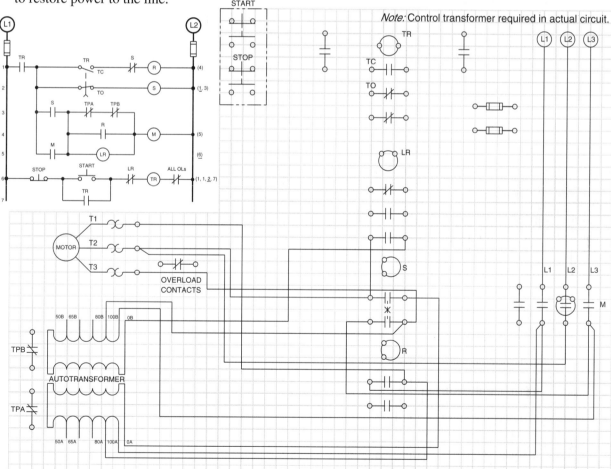

Reduced-Voltage Starting

Worksheet 17-5

Name _____ Date _____

Motor Load Monitoring

Use Data Sheet M on page 272 to complete the line diagram.

1. Draw the line diagram showing how a load guard power factor monitor may be added to a standard start/stop pushbutton circuit. The start/stop station controls the grinder, and the load guard automatically stops the motor when a jam or overload occurs.

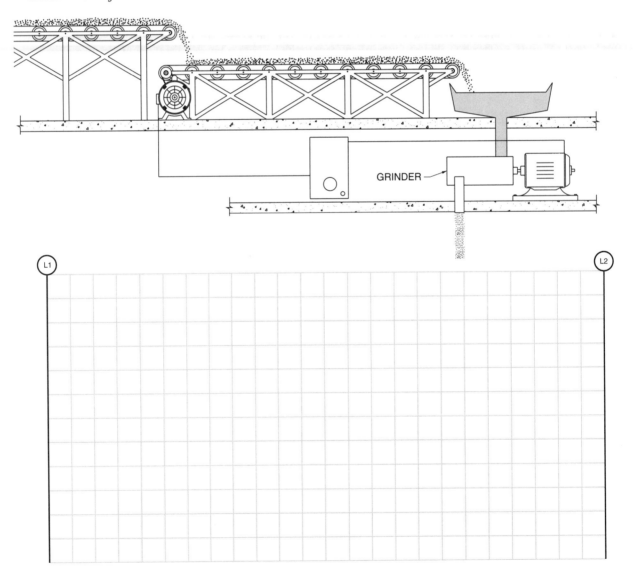

GRINDER

L1   L2

Reduced-Voltage Starting

Worksheet 17-6

Name _____ Date _____

Primary Resistor Reduced-Voltage Starting

1. Connect the power circuit from the transformer bank to the motor for high-voltage, reduced-voltage starting. Make all power circuit connections at the terminal screws. Connect the control transformer for 440 V to 110 V. Draw a control circuit that includes a two-position selector switch and a pressure switch. When the selector switch is in the automatic position, the motor is controlled by the pressure switch. The motor energizes at low pressure. When the selector switch is in the manual position, the motor is controlled by a start/stop pushbutton station. Include a light that indicates the motor is running at full voltage.

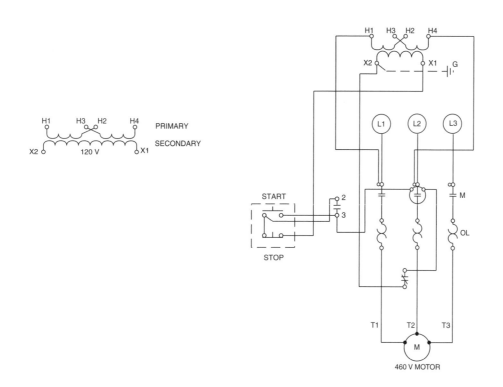

DUAL-VOLTAGE TRANSFORMER

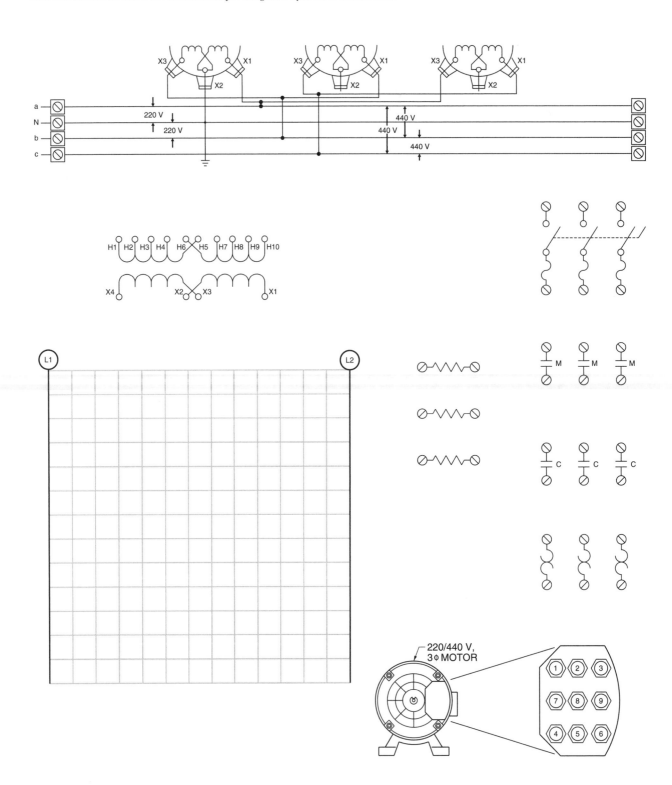

Reduced-Voltage Starting

Name _____ Date _____

Part-Winding Reduced-Voltage Starting

1. Connect the power circuit from the transformer bank to the motor for low-voltage, reduced-voltage starting. Make all power circuit connections at the terminal screws. Connect the control transformer for 208 V to 10 V. See Dual-Voltage Transformer on page 215. In the Part-Winding Reduced-Voltage Starting Circuit, the timer has both instantaneous and time-delay contacts. Use Data Sheet H on page 267. Do not change the operation of the circuit.

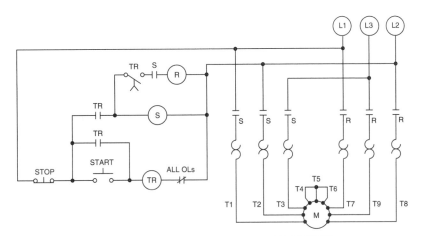

PART-WINDING REDUCED-VOLTAGE STARTING

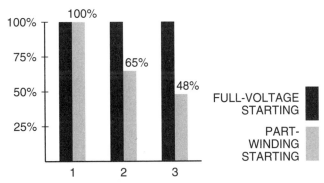

1 = VOLTAGE AT MOTOR
2 = LINE CURRENT WHEN STARTING
3 = STARTING TORQUE

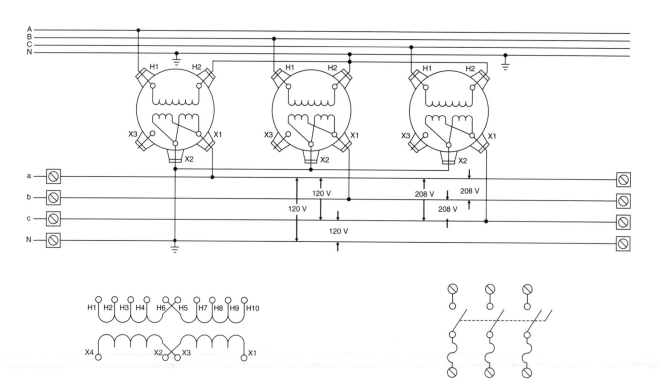

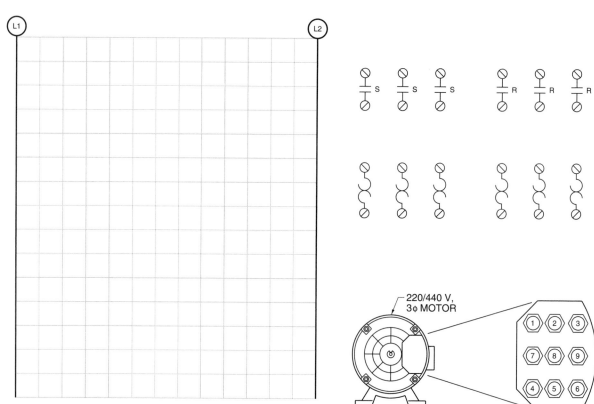

Reduced-Voltage Starting

Worksheet 17-8

Name _____ Date _____

Wye/Delta Reduced-Voltage Starting

1. Make all power terminal connections at the terminal screws. Draw a control circuit that includes a two-position selector switch and a temperature switch. When the selector switch is in the automatic position, the motor is controlled by the temperature switch. The motor energizes at high temperature. When the selector switch is in the manual position, the motor is controlled by a start/stop pushbutton station. Modify the circuit to include a timer that has only time-delay contacts. Use Data Sheet H on page 267. Connect the motor for reduced-voltage starting.

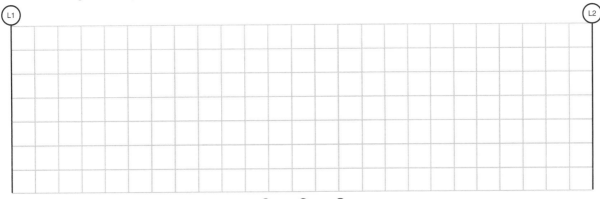

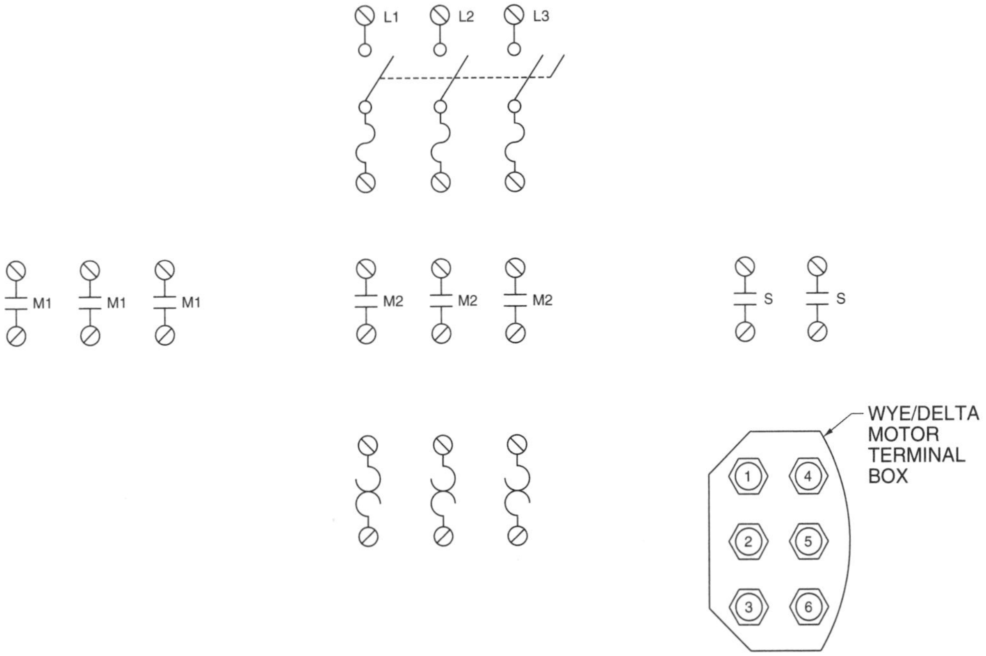

**Reduced-Voltage
Starting**

Worksheet 17-9

Name _____ Date _____

Closed Transition Reduced-Voltage Starting

1. Connect the motor for closed transition reduced-voltage starting. Make all power circuit connections at the terminal screws.

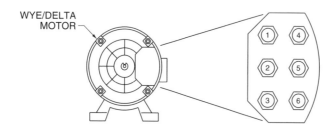

WYE/DELTA
MOTOR

Accelerating and Decelerating Methods

Tech-Chek 18

Name _____   Date _____

Electrical Motor Controls

_____ 1. Braking torque developed with friction brakes is directly proportional to the ___.
  A. speed of the motor   C. applied voltage
  B. surface area and spring   D. type of solenoid used
     pressure

_____ 2. The advantage of using friction brakes is ___.
  A. their ability to be connected   C. their ability to control loads that are often
     to any voltage   stopped
  B. simplified maintenance and   D. low maintenance
     lower initial cost

_____ 3. Electric braking is accomplished by applying ___ to the stationary windings once the AC is removed.

_____ 4. Dynamic braking is normally applied to DC motors because ___.

_____ 5. A combination of dynamic braking and friction braking can be used because ___.
  A. dynamic braking cannot   C. dynamic braking uses too much power
     hold a stopped load
  B. friction brakes are less   D. AC brakes cannot be used with DC
     expensive

_____ 6. A(n) ___ is a load that requires a constant torque/variable horsepower motor.
  A. air compressor   C. fan
  B. clock   D. conveyor

_____ 7. A ___ is a load that requires a constant horsepower/variable torque motor.
  A. paper roll machine   C. wood chipper
  B. ball mill   D. band saw

_____ 8. A ___ is a load that requires a variable torque/variable horsepower motor.
  A. lathe   C. fan
  B. vacuum pump   D. dryer

_____ 9. A(n) ___-delay timer is used in applications where the time needed to decelerate the motor is constant and known.

_____ 10. A motor used for plugging should have a service factor of ___ or more.

_____ 11. Electric braking is a method of braking in which a(n) ___ voltage is applied to the stationary windings of a motor after the AC voltage is removed.

_____ 12. ___ is the force that produces or tends to produce rotation in a motor.

_____ 13. In dynamic braking, the smaller the resistance of the resistor used, the ___ the rate of energy dissipation.

_____ 14. ___ is the torque a motor produces when the rotor is stationary and full power is applied to the motor.

_____ 15. Electric power is rated in horsepower or ___.

_____ 16. The applied frequency or ___ must be changed to change the speed of an AC induction motor.

_____ 17. An AC induction motor with four poles operating at 60 Hz runs at a synchronous speed of ___ rpm.

_____ 18. ___ circuit logic is a circuit that starts a motor in low speed and automatically brings the motor to high speed after the high pushbutton is pressed.

_____ 19. ___ circuit logic is a circuit that requires a motor to start at low speed before the motor can be put into high speed.

_____ 20. A(n) ___ changes standard AC voltage into DC voltage.

_____ 21. A(n) ___ changes DC voltage into AC voltage.

_____ 22. A(n) ___ can be used to change the output speed of a motor, provided the manufacturer limits are not exceeded.

_____ 23. ___ are used in very low-speed applications.

_____ 24. The work required to move a 150 lb load 10′ is ___ lb-ft.

_____ 25. A total of ___ lb-ft of torque is produced by a 75 lb force pushing on a 2′ lever arm.

_____ 26. The full-load torque of a ½ HP motor operating at 1725 rpm is ___ lb-ft.

_____ 27. An increase in a motor's speed causes a(n) ___ in the motor's horsepower output if the torque requirements on the motor remain constant.

_____ 28. An increase in a motor's torque requirement causes a(n) ___ in the motor's horsepower output if the speed remains constant.

_____ 29. A total of ___ lb-ft of torque is produced by a 100 lb force pushing on a 4′ lever arm.

_____ 30. The full-load torque of a 5 HP motor operating at 1725 rpm is ___ lb-ft.

_____ 31. The full-load torque of a 5 HP motor operating at 1140 rpm is ___ lb-ft.

_____ 32. A 460 V, 85% efficient motor pulling 6 A produces ___ HP.

_____ 33. A 230 V, 85% efficient motor pulling 12 A produces ___ HP.

_____ 34. The synchronous speed of a two-pole motor operating at 50 Hz is ___ rpm.

_____ 35. A(n) ___″ driven machine pulley diameter is required if a motor running at 1200 rpm has a 3″ pulley and the driven machine is running at 600 rpm.

_____ 36. A(n) ___″ driven machine pulley diameter is required if a motor running at 1200 rpm has a 3″ pulley and the driven machine is running at 2400 rpm.

_____ 37. ___ stop is a stopping method in which the level of voltage applied to a motor is reduced as the motor decelerates.

Accelerating and Decelerating Methods

Worksheet 18-1

Name _____   Date _____

Multispeed Starting

The circuit provides for multispeed starting using a constant-horsepower motor. The motor control is a three-element fast/slow/stop pushbutton station connected for starting in either the fast or slow speed. The stop pushbutton must be pressed first to change speed from fast to slow.

1. Complete the wiring diagram based on the line diagram. Do not make any wire splices or additional terminal connections on the wiring diagram. All connections must run from terminal screw to terminal screw.

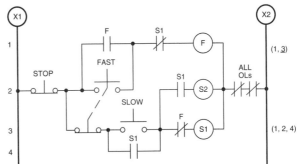

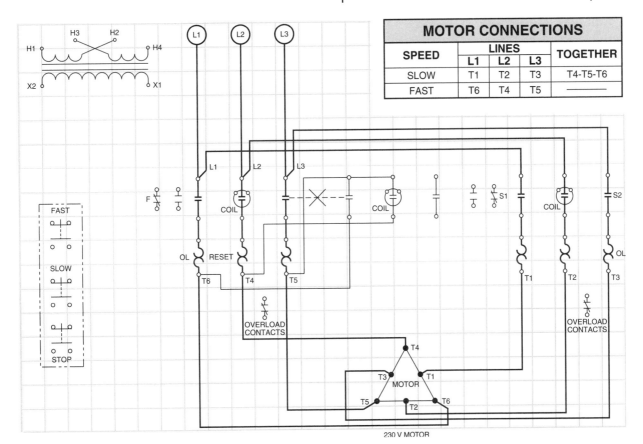

MOTOR CONNECTIONS				
SPEED	**LINES**			**TOGETHER**
	L1	**L2**	**L3**	
SLOW	T1	T2	T3	T4-T5-T6
FAST	T6	T4	T5	——

Accelerating and Decelerating Methods

Worksheet 18-2

Name _____ Date _____

Motor Plugging

The motor is started by pushing the start pushbutton. As the motor accelerates, centrifugal force closes the normally open contacts of the plugging switch. This closes relay CR1, which is held closed by its normally open contacts. The forward contactor (F) opens, closing the reverse contactor (R) through its normally closed auxiliary contacts and through the contacts of relay CR1 when the stop pushbutton is pressed. The reverse contactor applies reverse power to the motor until its speed is reduced to allow the contacts of the plugging switch to open. The opening of the contacts causes CR1 and R to open, disconnecting the motor from the line. Relay CR1 is a safety interlock that prevents the starter from energizing when the motor shaft is turned by hand.

1. Complete the wiring diagram based on the line diagram. Do not make any wire splices or additional terminal connections on the wiring diagram. All connections must run from terminal screw to terminal screw.

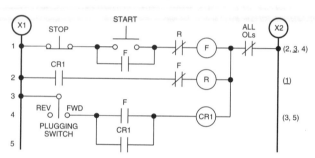

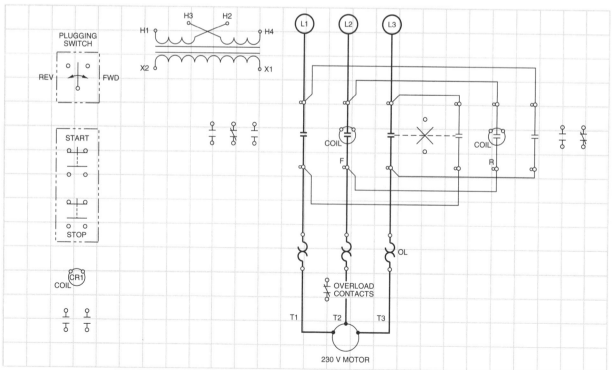

Accelerating and Decelerating Methods

Name _____   Date _____

Two-Speed Starting

The circuit provides for compelling, two-speed starting with two thermal overload relays, one for each speed. The controller is internally wired to compel the operator to start the motor at slow speed. It cannot be switched to fast speed until after the motor is running. The slow-speed contactor and the control relay (FR) are energized when the slow pushbutton is pressed. The motor does not start if the fast pushbutton is pressed because the normally closed contacts of the control relay prevent the high-speed contactor from energizing. Once the motor is running, pressing the fast pushbutton automatically opens the slow-speed contactor and closes the high-speed contactor through the normally closed contacts of the slow-speed contactor and the normally open contacts of the control relay. The starter cannot be switched from fast to slow without first pressing the stop pushbutton.

1. Complete the wiring diagram based on the line diagram. Do not make any wire splices or additional terminal connections on the wiring diagram. All connections must run from terminal screw to terminal screw.

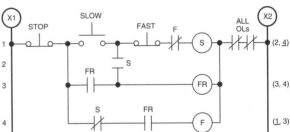

MOTOR CONNECTIONS			
SPEED	**LINES**		
	L1	**L2**	**L3**
SLOW	T1	T2	T3
FAST	T11	T12	T13

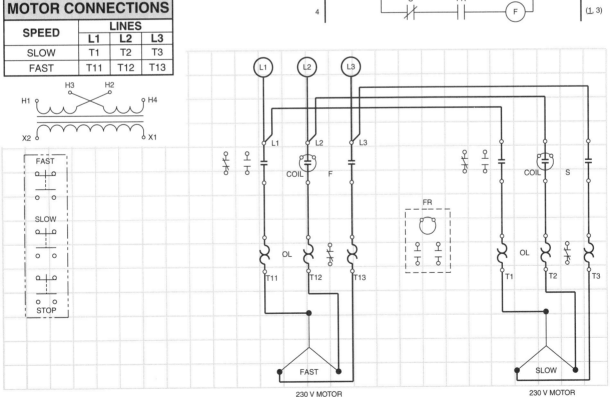

Accelerating and Decelerating Methods

Worksheet 18-4

Name _____ Date _____

Selective Multispeed Starting

The circuit provides for selective, multispeed starting with two thermal overload relays. The control is a three-element fast/slow/stop pushbutton station. The motor can be started at fast or slow speed but cannot be switched from fast to slow without first pressing the stop pushbutton.

1. Complete the wiring diagram based on the line diagram. Do not make any wire splices or additional terminal connections on the wiring diagram. All connections must run from terminal screw to terminal screw.

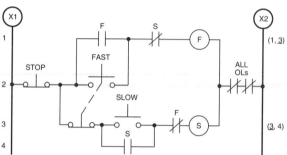

MOTOR CONNECTIONS

SPEED	LINES		
	L1	L2	L3
SLOW	T1	T2	T3
FAST	T11	T12	T13

230 V MOTOR

230 V MOTOR

Accelerating and Decelerating Methods

Worksheet 18-5

Name _____ Date _____

Unrestrictive Multispeed Starting

The motor control is a standard three-element fast/slow/stop pushbutton station connected for starting at either fast or slow speed. It cannot be switched from fast to slow without first pressing the stop pushbutton.

1. Complete the wiring diagram based on the line diagram. Do not make any wire splices or additional terminal connections on the wiring diagram. All connections must run from terminal screw to terminal screw.

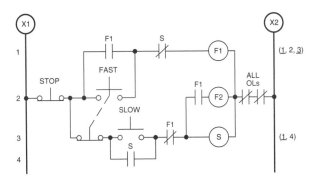

MOTOR CONNECTIONS				
SPEED	LINES			TOGETHER
	L1	L2	L3	
SLOW	T1	T2	T3	—
FAST	T6	T4	T5	T1-T2-T3

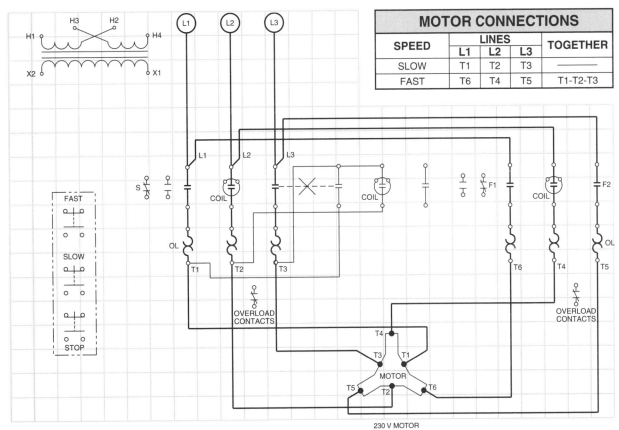

230 V MOTOR

Accelerating and Decelerating Methods

Worksheet 18-6

Name _____   Date _____

Compelling Circuit Logic

The motor must be started at low speed before changing to medium speed and must be running at medium speed before changing to high speed. Use two control relays to complete the circuit. Provide overload protection at all speeds.

1. Design a line diagram for compelling circuit logic using three motor starters (low, medium, and high). Use standard lettering, numbering, and coding information.

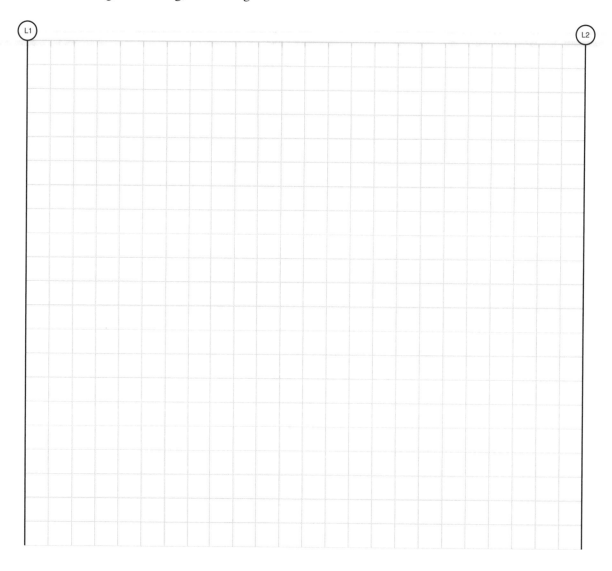

Accelerating and Decelerating Methods

Worksheet 18-7

Name _____   Date _____

Dynamic Braking

The friction brake is to be applied 3 sec after the motor is turned OFF, allowing the dynamic braking action to first slow the motor. The friction brake is to remain ON, holding the load until the motor is started again.

1. Design a circuit in which a friction brake can be applied to a DC shunt motor wired for dynamic braking. Use standard lettering, numbering, and coding information.

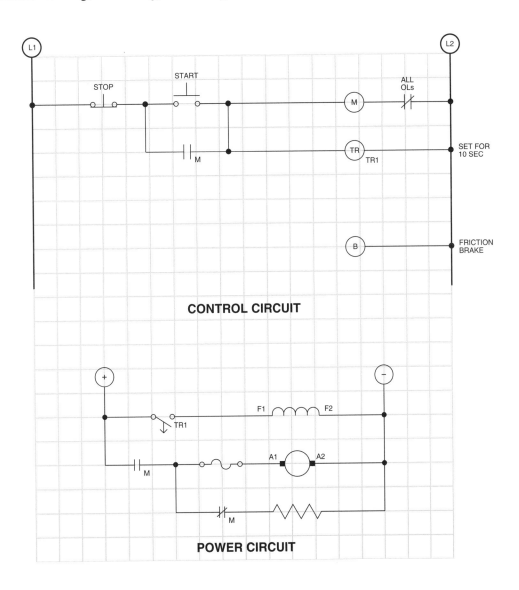

Accelerating and Decelerating Methods

Worksheet 18-8

Name _____   Date _____

Motor Temperature Control

Include a plugging switch which automatically turns OFF the heating element contactor if the circulating fan is not operating. Provide overload protection for the motor.

1. Design a circuit in which a temperature switch turns ON and OFF a heating element and circulating fan based on a given temperature. Use standard lettering, numbering, and coding information.

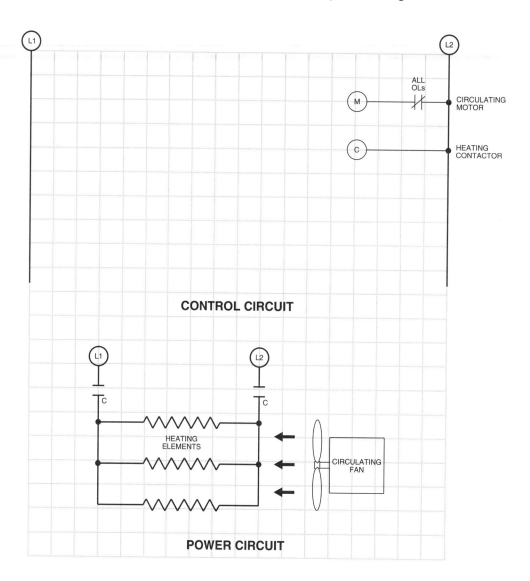

Accelerating and Decelerating Methods

Worksheet 18-9

Name _____ Date _____

One-Direction Motor Plugging

Plugging is a method of motor braking in which motor connections are reversed so the motor develops a counter-torque that acts as a braking force. Plugging a motor to a rapid stop is done with a plugging switch. Plugging is used for emergency stops to protect personnel when a motor must be stopped quickly.

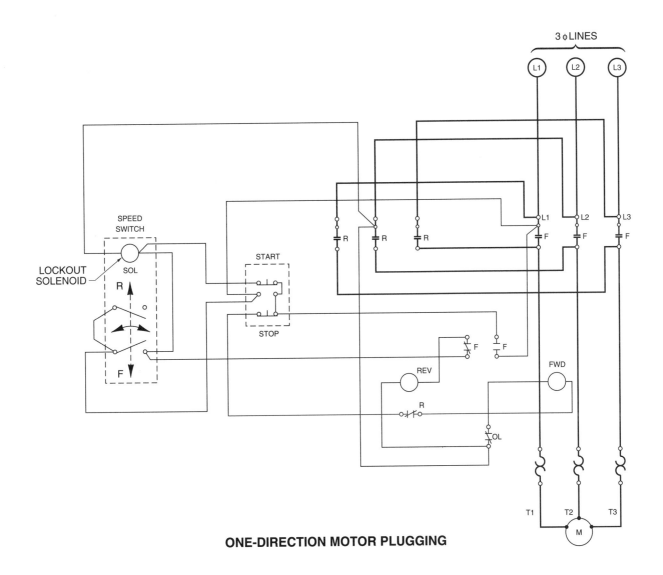

ONE-DIRECTION MOTOR PLUGGING

1. Draw the line diagram of one-direction motor plugging.

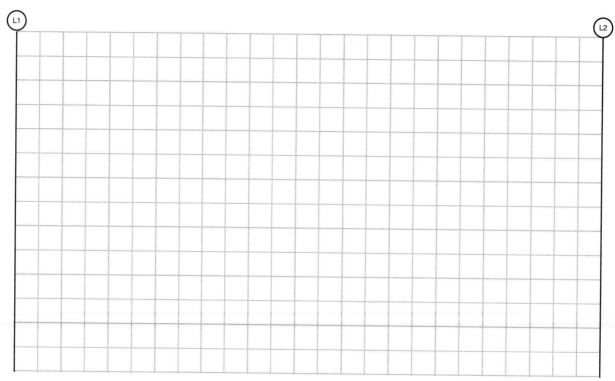

CIRCUIT 1

2. Redraw Circuit 1, adding a second stop pushbutton and a second start pushbutton.

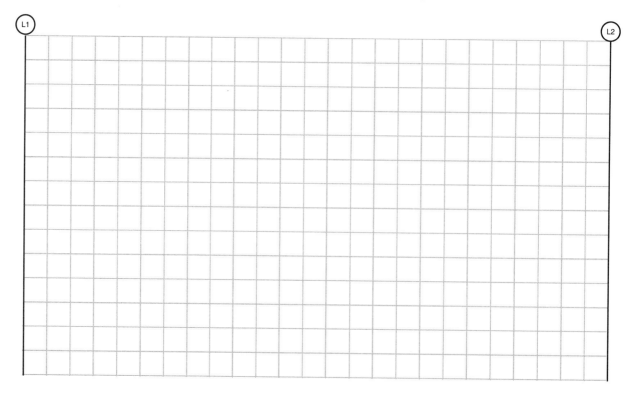

Accelerating and Decelerating Methods

Worksheet 18-10

Name _____ Date _____

Two-Direction Motor Plugging

In some applications, a motor must be brought to a rapid stop in either direction. A two-direction plugging switch is used when a motor must be plugged to a stop in either direction.

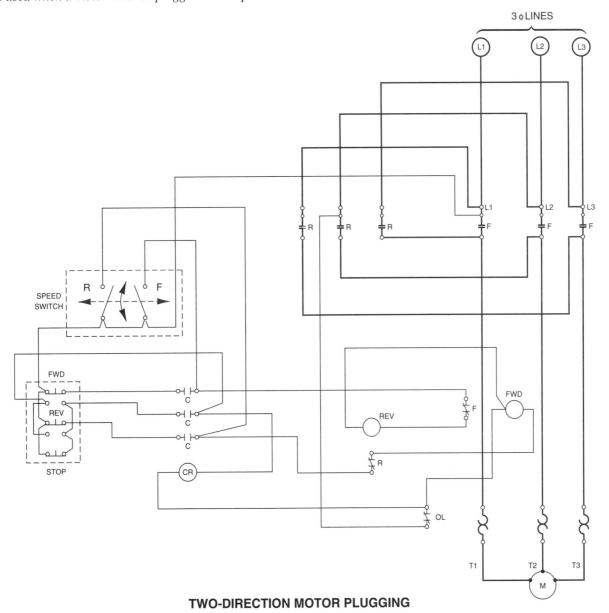

TWO-DIRECTION MOTOR PLUGGING

1. Draw the line diagram of two-direction motor plugging.

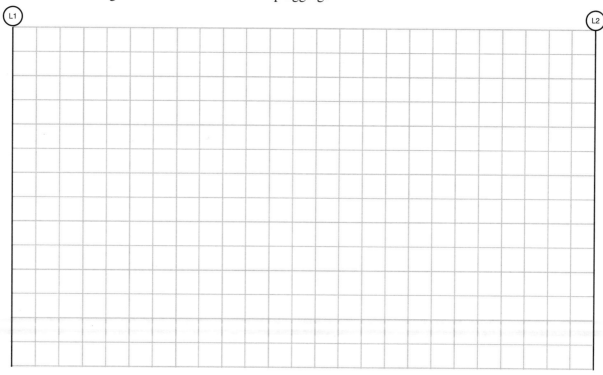

CIRCUIT 1

2. Redraw Circuit 1, adding a second forward pushbutton and a second reverse pushbutton. Include a yellow light to indicate that the motor is running in the forward direction and a red light to indicate the motor is running in the reverse direction.

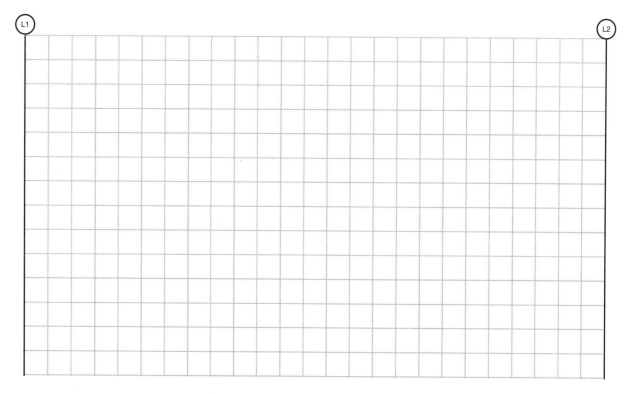

Accelerating and Decelerating Methods

Name _____ Date _____

Two-Speed Separate Winding Motors

A motor must have separate windings to be able to run at different speeds. The motor speed changes when power is applied to different windings.

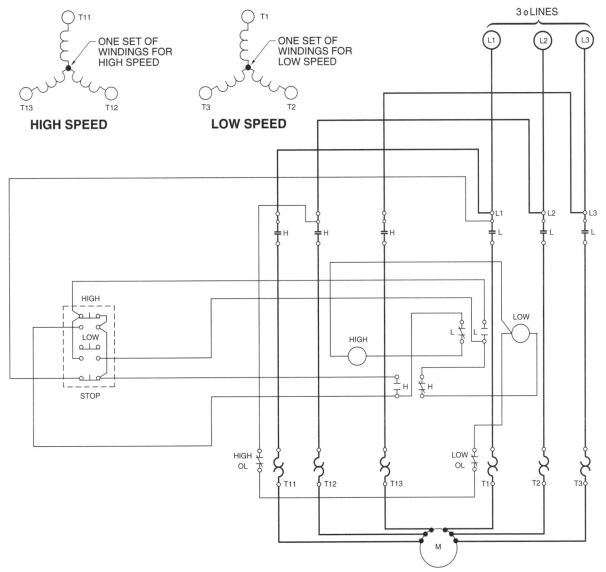

TWO-SPEED SEPARATE WINDING MOTOR

1. Draw the line diagram of the two-speed separate winding motor. *Note:* The stop pushbutton must be pressed before changing speeds.

CIRCUIT 1

2. Redraw Circuit 1, adding a red light to indicate the motor is running in high speed. Add a green light to indicate the motor is running in low speed. Include a temperature switch that automatically places the motor in high speed when a setpoint temperature is reached. Do not remove the high-speed pushbutton. The high-speed pushbutton is used to manually place the motor in high speed.

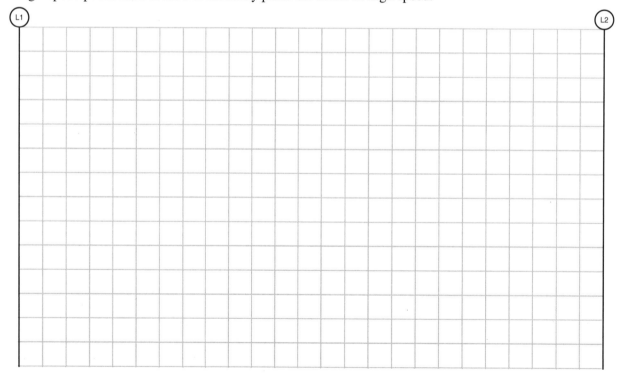

Preventive Maintenance and Troubleshooting

Tech-Chek 19

Name _____ Date _____

Electrical Motor Controls

_____ **1.** Phase unbalance in a 3φ power system normally occurs because ___ the system.
   A. 3φ loads are removed from   C. 1φ loads are applied to
   B. 3φ loads are added to   D. 1φ loads are removed from

_____ **2.** A ___ motor continues to run with a phase loss.
   A. 1φ   C. DC
   B. 3φ   D. capacitor-run

_____ **3.** The NEC® requires protection against ___ on all equipment transporting people.
   A. phase loss   C. phase unbalance
   B. phase reversal   D. single-phasing

_____ **4.** ___ is the major cause of large voltage surges on power lines.
   A. Frequency variation   C. A 3φ motor being turned OFF
   B. A lightning strike   D. A 1φ motor being turned OFF

_____ **5.** A(n) ___ system is the organization and management of commonly used parts, vendors and suppliers, and purchasing records in the preventive maintenance system.

_____ **6.** A low ___ indicates excessive moisture or contamination in the motor insulation.

_____ **7.** The major cause of most motor failures is ___.
   A. capacitor failure   C. bearing failure
   B. mechanical breakage   D. excessive heat

_____ **8.** A(n) ___ detects motor insulation and deterioration before a motor fails.

_____ **9.** A(n) ___ test is used to check motor insulation over the life of the motor.
   A. insulation spot   C. insulation step voltage
   B. dielectric absorption   D. phase-loss

_____ **10.** A(n) ___ test is used to check for moisture and contamination on insulation.
   A. insulation spot   C. insulation step voltage
   B. dielectric absorption   D. phase-loss

_____ **11.** The series field in a DC motor normally has a reading ___ the armature reading.
   A. greater than   C. the same as
   B. less than   D. cannot be determined

_____ **12.** The shunt field normally has a reading ___ the armature reading.
   A. greater than   C. the same as
   B. less than   D. cannot be determined

Voltage Identification

_____ **1.** Half-wave DC

_____ **2.** Full-wave DC

_____ **3.** 1φ

_____ **4.** 3φ

_____ **5.** Pure DC

_____ **6.** Semifiltered DC

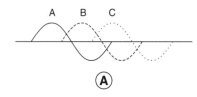

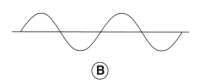

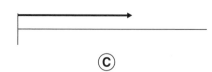

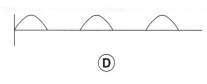

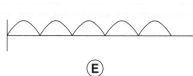

Motor Insulation Tests

_____ **1.** Curve ___ indicates good
motor insulation.

_____ **2.** Curve ___ indicates good
motor insulation.

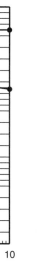

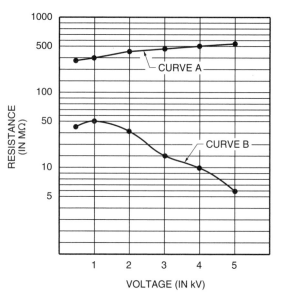

Preventive Maintenance and Troubleshooting

Name _____   Date _____

Motor Protection

Use Data Sheet N on page 273 to complete the wiring diagram and line diagram.

1. Design a circuit using the start/stop pushbutton station and a Model N relay to protect against phase loss or phase angle error (adjustable from 5° to 15°). Phase angle error takes place in an unbalanced system. The relay is rated for the same voltage as the power lines. Connect the relay so it adds protection along with the motor starter overloads.

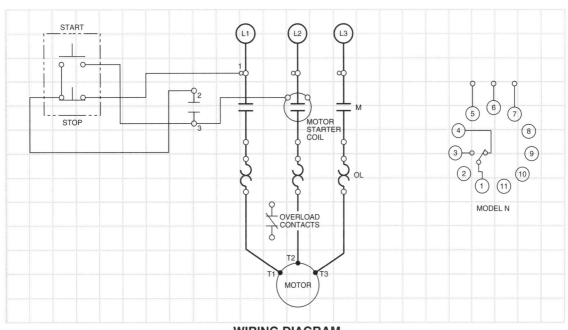

WIRING DIAGRAM

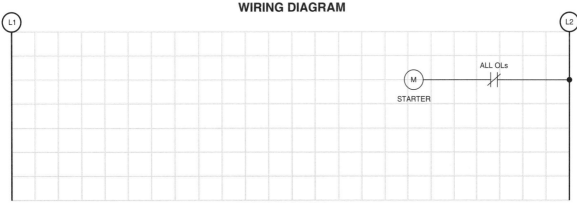

LINE DIAGRAM

Preventive Maintenance and Troubleshooting

Worksheet 19-2

Name _____ Date _____

Phase Loss Protection

Use Data Sheet O on page 274 to complete the wiring diagram and line diagram.

1. Design a circuit using the start/stop pushbutton station and a Model O relay to de-energize the motor starter if one or more phases are lost. The relay also de-energizes the motor starter if the phase sequence is not correct. L1 (R) must be connected to pin 5. L2 (S) must be connected to pin 6. L3 (T) must be connected to pin 7. Any other sequence de-energizes the relay. Connect the relay so it adds protection along with the overload contacts.

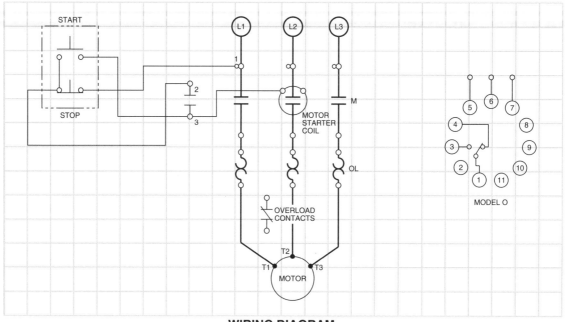

WIRING DIAGRAM

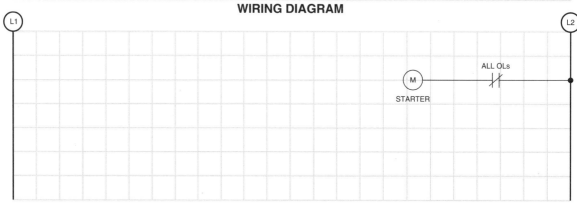

LINE DIAGRAM

Preventive Maintenance and Troubleshooting

Worksheet 19-3

Name _____ Date _____

Overload Protection

Use Data Sheet P on page 275 to complete the wiring diagrams and line diagrams.

1. Design a circuit using the start/stop pushbutton station and a Model P relay to protect against an overload in the power circuit. The relay can be used on 1ϕ or 3ϕ circuits. It uses a current transformer that detects the amount of current in any wire that passes through the current transformer. It can be used with or in place of the standard overload heater found on magnetic motor starters. The exact setting of the relay, like the selection of overload heaters, must meet NEC® requirements. The maximum setpoint of the relay is normally 1.15 or 1.25 times the FLC, which is found on the nameplate of the motor. For exact requirements, see Article 430 of the NEC®.

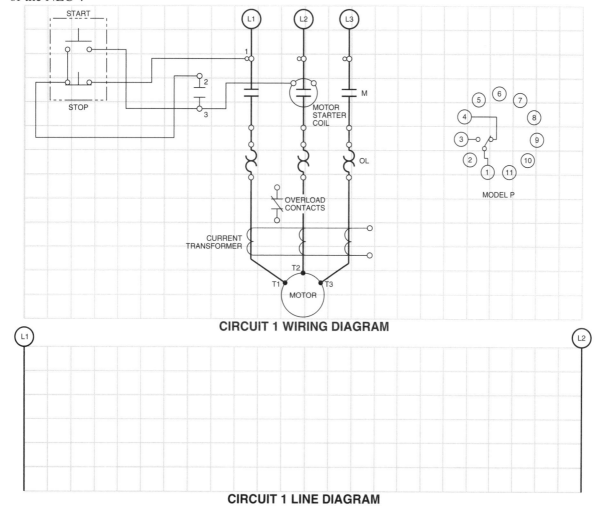

CIRCUIT 1 WIRING DIAGRAM

CIRCUIT 1 LINE DIAGRAM

2. Redraw the line diagram of Circuit 1, adding a timer to allow the locked rotor current to exist for 5 sec before the relay monitors the full-load current. This is required because the relay reacts instantly to an overload current and turns OFF the motor. This does not allow the locked rotor current required to start the motor.

CIRCUIT 2 LINE DIAGRAM

3. Redraw the line diagram of Circuit 2, adding a second timer to allow a full-load overload current for 10 sec before the motor is automatically turned OFF. Thus, timer 1 allows the locked rotor current (starting current) to exist for 5 sec and timer 2 allows the full-load current (running current) to exist for 10 sec before the motor is automatically turned OFF.

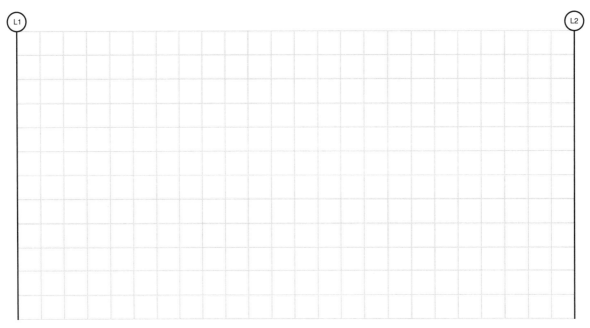

Preventive Maintenance and Troubleshooting

Worksheet 19-4

Name _____ Date _____

Manual/Automatic Circuit Troubleshooting

Troubleshoot the circuit based on the given information.

1. The solenoid energizes when the pushbutton or pressure switch is closed. The pilot light does not turn ON when the foot switch and temperature switch close. Add a fused jumper wire to the circuit to eliminate trouble with the control switches. Assume that the light does not light when the jumper wire is in place. Circle the part of the circuit that contains the fault.

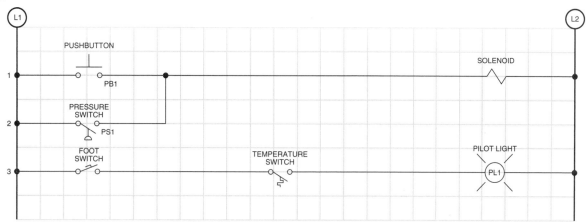

CIRCUIT 1

2. Redraw Circuit 1, adding a pushbutton that can be used to test PL1 anytime it is pressed.

Preventive Maintenance and Troubleshooting

Worksheet 19-5

Name _____ Date _____

Carton Fill Circuit Troubleshooting

Troubleshoot the circuit based on the given information.

1. The empty cartons are stopping and staying in place for the given amount of time when they hit the limit switch. The cartons are not being filled. Add a DMM set to measure voltage to the circuit to test the solenoid valve. Assume that the DMM indicates a proper voltage reading at the correct time. Circle the part of the circuit that contains the fault.

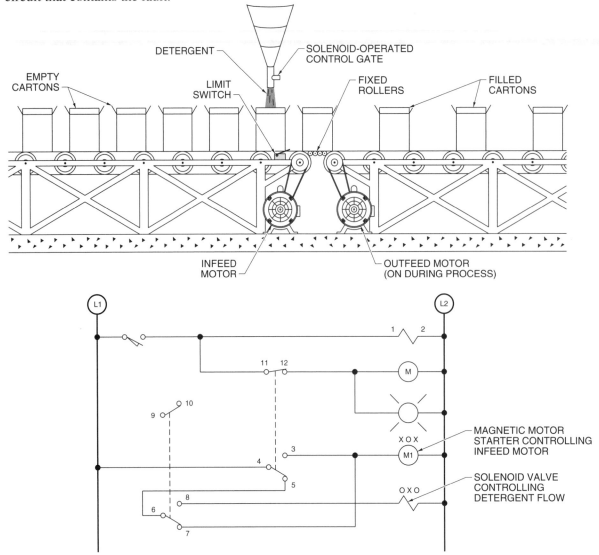

Preventive Maintenance
and Troubleshooting

Worksheet 19-6

Name _____ Date _____

Multiple Starter Circuit Troubleshooting
Troubleshoot the circuit based on the given information.

1. Warning light PL2 is ON. A check of starting coil M2 indicates that the starter is energized and the motor is running. Circle the part of the circuit that contains the fault.

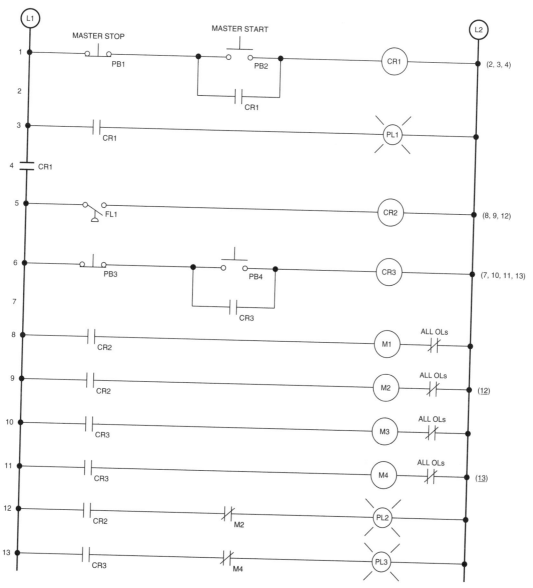

Preventive Maintenance and Troubleshooting

Worksheet 19-7

Name _____   Date _____

Primary Resistor Starting Circuit Troubleshooting

Troubleshoot the circuit based on the given information.

1. The motor is running hot and does not seem to have much power. A test with a DMM set to measure voltage indicates that there is only about one-half the required voltage at terminals T1, T2, and T3 of the motor. Add a fused jumper(s) to eliminate trouble with the control circuit. Connect the DMM to test the power circuit for the source of trouble.

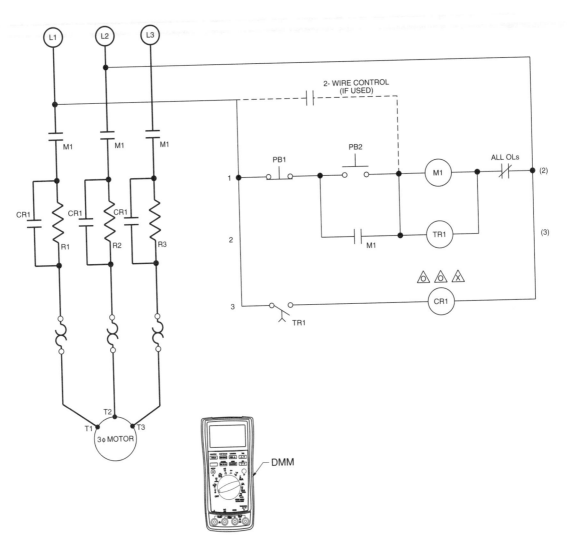

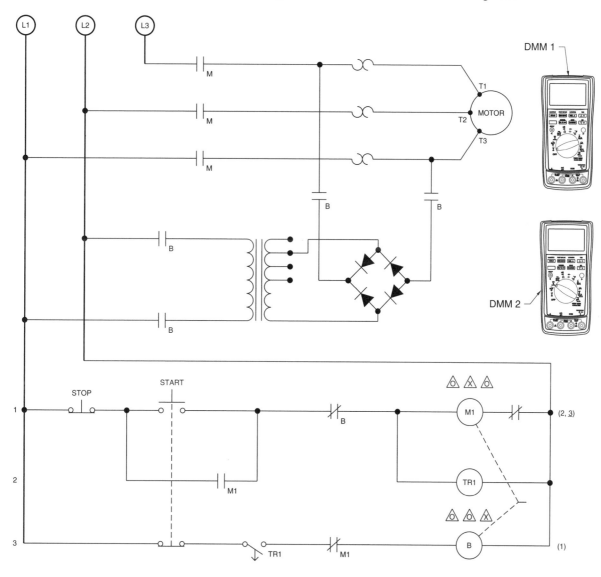

Preventive Maintenance and Troubleshooting

Worksheet 19-8

Name _____ Date _____

Motor Braking Circuit Troubleshooting
Troubleshoot the circuit based on the given information.

1. The motor is not braking to a stop. A test of the brake contactor in the control circuit indicates that the contactor is energizing at the correct time. Connect DMM 1 to test for the correct AC output from the transformer. Connect DMM 2 to test for the correct DC output when the brake contactor is energized.

Preventive Maintenance and Troubleshooting

Worksheet 19-9

Name _____   Date _____

Selector Switch Circuit Troubleshooting
Troubleshoot the circuit based on the given information.

1. Magnetic starter coil M1 starts and remains engaged after the start pushbutton is pressed, regardless of the position of the selector switch. Circle the part of the circuit that contains the fault.

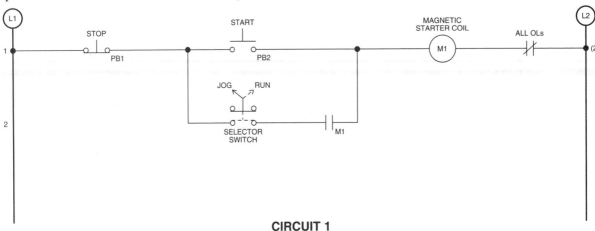

CIRCUIT 1

2. Redraw Circuit 1, adding a red lamp that is ON anytime the selector switch is in the run position and a yellow lamp that is ON anytime the selector switch is in the jog position. Only one lamp is ON at a time.

electrical motor controls *for Integrated Systems*

Appendix

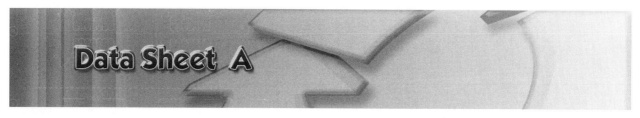

Wire Numbers

A control circuit may consist of a few individual wires or several thousand interconnected wires. Tracing one wire may be impossible without a system for keeping track of each wire in the circuit. The standard industrial wiring numbering system gives each wire or common group of wires a number. A common group is any wires that are connected directly without being broken by a device such as a pushbutton, contact, or starting coil.

Numbers are assigned in ascending numerical order (1, 2, 3, etc.), beginning with the upper left corner and moving to the right, line by line. A new number is assigned whenever a wire (or common group of wires) is broken by an electric device. See Figure A1.

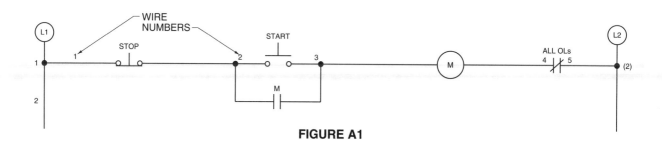

FIGURE A1

The first wire is assigned 1 and is referred to as wire 1 until it is broken by the stop pushbutton. After the stop pushbutton, wire 2 begins and continues until it is broken by the start pushbutton and the M contact. The wire going to the start pushbutton and the wire going to the M contact are referred to as wire 2 because wire 2 has not been broken by an electric device.

After the start pushbutton and the M contact, both wires are referred to as wire 3 until broken by the M starting coil. Wire 4 is assigned after the starting coil and continues until it is broken by the overload contacts. Wire 5 is the wire from the overload contacts to L2.

As a circuit's complexity increases, the numbers continue to ascend from the top left to the bottom right, line by line. See Figure A2. In this circuit, seven numbers are assigned. Some are assigned to individual wires and some to common groups of wires. A new number is assigned each time the interconnected wires are broken by an electric device.

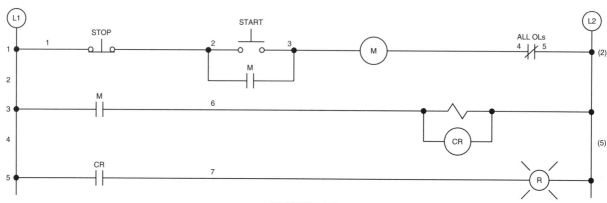

FIGURE A2

Wire Numbering System Simplification

In Figures A1 and A2, each wire was assigned a number regardless of its purpose or location in the circuit. Although this procedure is followed for some circuits, most circuits follow a simplified numbering system. In the simplified numbering system, any wire prewired by the manufacturer prior to shipping is not numbered. For example, the wire connecting the motor starting coil to the overload contacts is normally prewired and does not require an assigned number. See Figure A3.

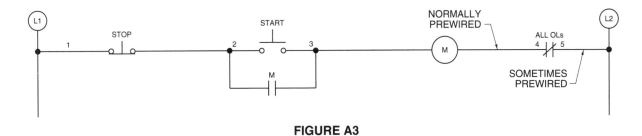

FIGURE A3

The numbering system may be further simplified by not numbering the wire directly connected to L2. This is because the wire from the overload contact to L2 is often prewired. The wire from L1 is always numbered.

The numbering system used for a given circuit applies to that circuit only. Numbering can differ from one circuit to another, even if the circuits are electrically identical. For example, three circuits that are electrically identical may be numbered differently. See Figure A4.

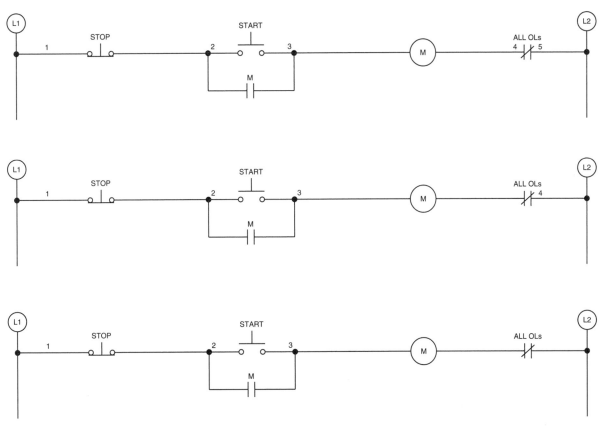

FIGURE A4

Wire Numbering System Advantages

The use of a wire numbering system simplifies initial circuit wiring and subsequent troubleshooting. The need for such a system becomes apparent when working on a wiring diagram in which wires enter and exit the conduit and are often grouped with many other wires.

Another advantage of a wire numbering system is that its use by manufacturers allows them to provide illustrations of connections for different wiring combinations. See Figure A5. The wiring diagram is provided by the motor starter manufacturer when the motor starter is purchased with an enclosure. The manufacturer includes the diagram on the inside cover of the enclosure. All major manufacturers use the standard wire numbering system described with only slight variations.

In Figure A5, the manufacturer has prewired the motor coil to one side of the overload contacts. The other side of the overload contacts is connected directly to L2 and is marked X2. The separate control note explains why the contact is marked X2.

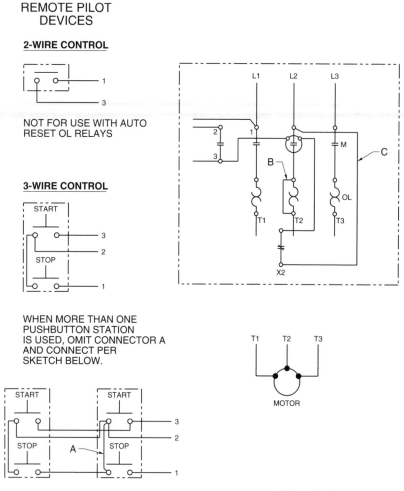

FIGURE A5

The prewiring is left alone if the starting coil is the same voltage level as the supply lines (L1 and L2). Wire C is removed from L2 if the starting coil is not the same voltage level as the supply lines, or if a separate control supply is used. For example, if a 120 V starting coil controls a 240 V motor, L1 and L2 must be 240 V to power the motor. In this case, wire C must be removed and connected to a 120 V supply. For this reason, X2 is marked on the overload indicating a connection to a lower supply voltage.

In Figure A5, the manufacturer has marked wire points 1, 2, and 3 on the diagram. These numbers are standard and are marked directly on all starters from major manufacturers. The starter may be wired for 2-wire, 3-wire, or multiple-control stations with each point marked in this manner. For example, if a 2-wire device, such as a pressure, float, or temperature switch, is used to control the motor, the control device is connected to points 1 and 3. If a 3-wire control device, such as a pushbutton station, is used to control the motor, it is connected to points 1, 2, and 3.

As circuits become more complicated, it is impossible for manufacturers to apply a standard numbering system to every circuit. Instead, the electrician must number the wires in each circuit at the time of wiring. Exceptions are circuits that are used frequently, such as circuits that forward and reverse a motor with a standard start/stop pushbutton station. In this case, the manufacturer may provide the wire numbering.

Line Diagrams Used to Connect Wiring Diagrams

The basic language of control is the line diagram. Its function is to illustrate quickly and concisely how the control circuit is to perform electrically. The wiring diagram of a circuit can be completed by using the circuit's line diagram. Unlike a line diagram, a wiring diagram shows as closely as possible the actual connections and placement of all components in the circuit.

For example, a standard start/stop pushbutton station with memory is shown by its line diagram. The wiring diagram of the same circuit shows all connections of all components, even those that are present but not used in this particular circuit. See Figure A6. For example, the NC start contacts, NO stop contacts, and the NC auxiliary contacts on the starter are included but not used in the circuit.

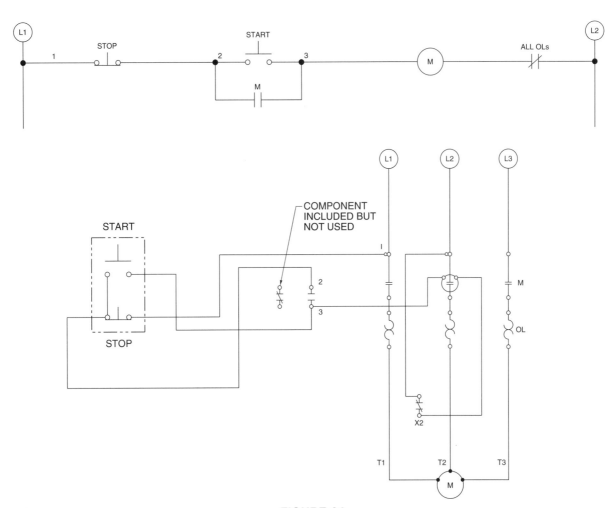

FIGURE A6

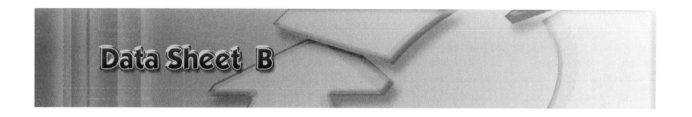

Fluid Power Cylinder Control

The operation of a fluid power cylinder may be controlled by two limit switches and a solenoid-operated valve. See Figure B1. The line diagram illustrates the connections for each piece of electrical equipment.

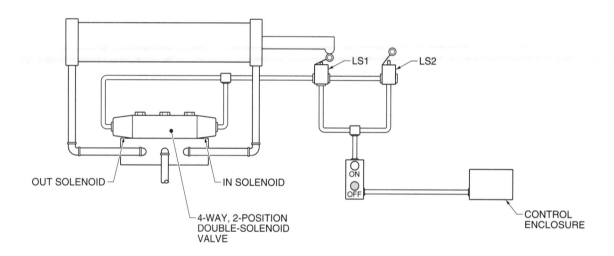

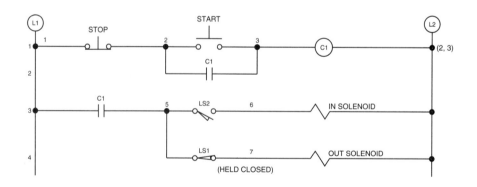

FIGURE B1

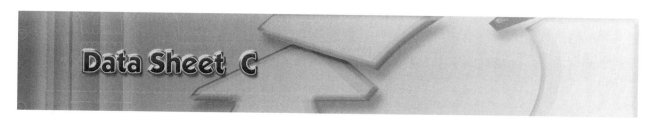

Data Sheet C

Level Control Relay

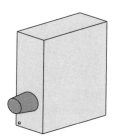

MODEL C

- Level control for conductive liquids
- Max.-min. control of discharging
- Adjustable sensitivity
- 10 A SPDT output relay
- LED-indication for relay ON
- AC or DC supply voltage

SPECIFICATIONS

Sensitivity
Knob-adjustable sensitivity
with relative scale.

ON from 3.5 kΩ to 25 kΩ
OFF from 8 kΩ to 45 kΩ

Sensor voltage
Max. 24 VAC

Sensor current
Max. 2.5 mA

Connection cable between sensor and amplifier
2- or 3-core plastic cable, normally unscreened.
Cable length: Max. 100 m

Resistance between cores and ground must be
at least 220 kΩ.

In certain cases, use a screened cable between
sensor and amplifier, where cable is placed
parallel to load cables. Screen is connected to
pin 7.

WIRING DIAGRAMS

Example 1

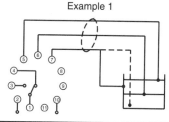

Example 2

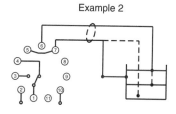

MODE OF OPERATION

Max. and/or min. control for discharging of
conductive liquids.
Relay for control of charging.

Example 1
Level control is connected as max. and
min. control (registration of two levels).
Relay operates when liquid reaches max.
electrode (pin 5), provided that min. electrode
is in contact with liquid.

Relay releases when min. electrode is no
longer in contact with liquid. Pin 7 must be
connected to container. If container consists
of a non-conductive material, an additional
electrode must be used which is connected to
pin 7. This electrode is shown by the dotted line.

Example 2
Level control is connected as max. or min.
control (registration of 1 level).
Relay operates when electrode (pin 6) is in
contact with liquid. An additional electrode must
be used if container consists of a non-conductive
material (to be connected to pin 7).

EXAMPLE 1 OPERATIONAL DIAGRAM

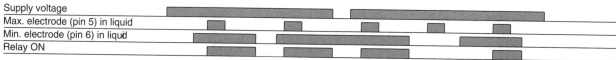

Supply voltage	
Max. electrode (pin 5) in liquid	
Min. electrode (pin 6) in liquid	
Relay ON	

EXAMPLE 2 OPERATIONAL DIAGRAM

Supply voltage	
Min. electrode (pin 6) in liquid	
Relay ON	

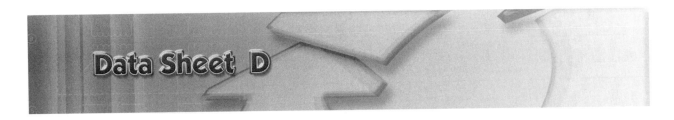

Data Sheet D

Reversing Motor Circuits

Electricians are required to wire a variety of AC and DC motors to run in forward and reverse. Wiring the motors can be confusing when the motor wiring diagram is new or unfamiliar. In addition, almost every motor manufacturer provides only one basic diagram. Modifications such as reversing are listed as printed information below the wiring diagram. Thus, the electrician must convert the wiring diagram and written instructions into a circuit that properly reverses the motor.

Basic Wiring Rules

A basic wiring procedure may be modified to develop the proper circuitry to wire any AC or DC motor to run in forward and reverse at any voltage. A wiring diagram can be developed for any motor in just a few minutes after applying the basic wiring procedure to several situations. Basic wiring rules are required before learning the basic wiring procedure. Basic wiring rules include:

- Every hot lead must be switched. The hot lead (ungrounded conductor) must be switched so that the power is never applied to the motor in the OFF position. See Figure D1.
- A motor must be connected for only one voltage. Motors are often designed with multiple windings for different voltages. Always wire the motor for the proper voltage in the specific case.
- A motor must be connected so that it cannot be electrically connected to run simultaneously in forward and reverse directions. Wiring diagrams must provide for the motor to run in only one direction at a time or the motor or power source may be severely damaged.
- A motor must be connected so that it cannot be electrically connected to run simultaneously at different speeds. For a multispeed motor, wiring diagrams must provide for the motor to run at only one speed at a time or the motor or power source may be severely damaged.

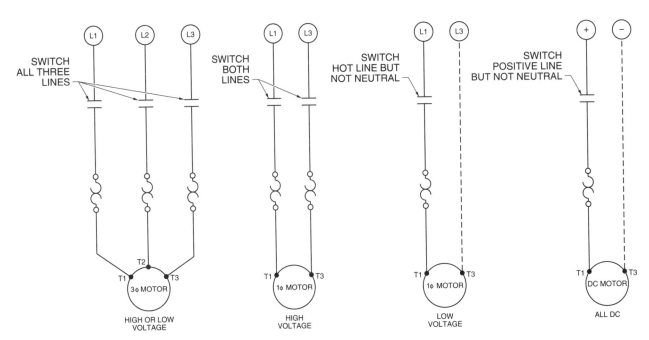

FIGURE D1

Basic Wiring Procedure

Seven steps are necessary for wiring any AC or DC motor to run in forward and reverse.

1. Develop a motor objective. Determine exactly what the wiring diagram is to accomplish. Select only one of the two voltage connections illustrated on the motor. For example, assume that a motor must be connected so that it runs in forward and reverse by means of a magnetic controller.

2. Obtain information from the motor nameplate. The motor nameplate provides information for two voltage supplies See Figure D2. The nameplate information on a typical 3ϕ motor shows that it can be wired for 220 V or 480 V. The low-voltage information provided on the motor nameplate is used if the supply voltage required is 220 V.

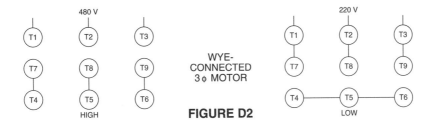

FIGURE D2

3. Make a written diagram of the circuit objective showing exactly how each wire must be connected to accomplish the objective. Put the wiring connections into words. See Figure D3. Follow the manufacturer's wiring diagram and interchange L1 and L3 as specified by NEMA standards.

Forward	Reverse
L1 to T1 and T7	L1 to T3 and T9
L2 to T2 and T8	L2 to T2 and T8
L3 to T3 and T9	L3 to T1 and T7
T4 to T5 to T6	T4 to T5 to T6

FIGURE D3

4. Remove common connections that are not power lines. To simplify the written diagram (or objective), remove any connection that is not the same in forward and reverse, provided it is not the power line. For example, connections T4, T5, and T6 can be removed because they are the same in forward and reverse. Connections L2, T2, and T8 cannot be removed because L2 is a power line and must be switched. See Figure D4.

Forward	Reverse
L1 to T1 and T7	L1 to T3 and T9
L2 to T2 and T8	L2 to T2 and T8
L3 to T3 and T9	L3 to T1 and T7

FIGURE D4

5. Use one name for the remaining common connections. To further simplify the written objective, use one name for any combination of wires that appears in the same direction on both sides of the objective (forward and reverse). For example, T1 and T7 = T1, T2 and T8 = T2, and T3 and T9 = T3. This simplifies the forward and reverse connections. See Figure D5.

Forward	Reverse
L1 to T1	L1 to T3
L2 to T2	L2 to T2
L3 to T3	L3 to T1

FIGURE D5

6. Convert the written objective into a diagram that shows the placement of electric contacts. The wiring diagram may be determined once the simplified written diagram of the objective is developed. A set of electric contacts is needed every place the word "to" appears in the written objective. See Figure D6.

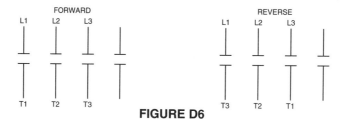

FIGURE D6

7. Draw the wiring diagram. To draw the wiring diagram, only the connections between any two motor or power lines that are the same are required. For example, L1 on the forward side is connected to L1 on the reverse side. Likewise, T1 on the forward side is connected to T1 on the reverse side. The wiring diagram is complete when all the lines are drawn. See Figure D7.

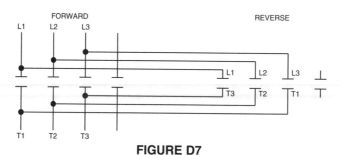

FIGURE D7

Single-Phase Motor Example

Use the nameplate information for a typical 1ϕ motor that can be wired for 115 V or 230 V to develop the wiring diagram. See Figure D8.

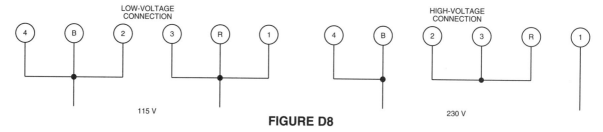

FIGURE D8

1. Develop a motor objective. The objective is to connect a motor to run in forward or reverse by means of a manual controller.

2. Obtain information from the motor nameplate. Assume a supply voltage of 115 V. Obtain the appropriate information from the motor nameplate.

3. Make a written diagram of the objective. See Figure D9. Note: The objective has not been simplified. Do not combine steps or simplify the objective too early. Power lines must be switched, therefore, each must be listed separately. The two wires to be interchanged are black and red (B and R). Consequently, they have to be listed separately and should not be connected to any other wire.

Forward	Reverse
B to 4 and 2	R to 4 and 2
R to 3 and 1	B to 3 and 1
L1 to 4 and 2	L1 to 4 and 2
L2 to 3 and 1	L2 to 3 and 1

FIGURE D9

4. Remove common connections that are not power lines. See Figure D10.

Forward	Reverse
B to 4 and 2	R to 4 and 2
R to 3 and 1	B to 3 and 1
L1 to 4 and 2	L1 to 4 and 2

FIGURE D10

5. Use one name for the remaining common connections. See Figure D11.

Forward	Reverse
B to 4	R to 4
R to 3	B to 3
L1 to 4	L1 to 4

FIGURE D11

6. Convert the written objective into a diagram that shows the placement of electrical contacts. See Figure D12.

FIGURE D12

7. Draw the wiring diagram. See Figure D13.

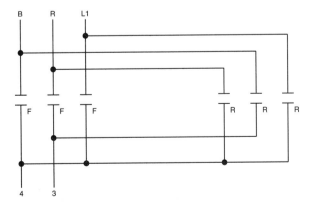

FIGURE D13

Single-Phase, Dual-Voltage, Capacitor-Start Motor Example

Use the nameplate information for a typical 1φ, dual-voltage, capacitor-start motor to develop the wiring diagram for both voltage levels. See Figure D14.

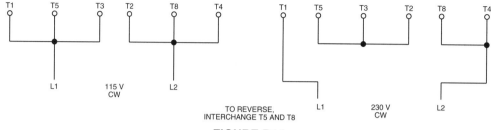

FIGURE D14

1. Develop a motor objective. The objective is to connect a motor to run in forward or reverse by means of a manual controller.
2. Obtain information from the motor nameplate. Two wiring diagrams are required, one for a supply voltage of 115 V and one for a supply voltage of 230 V. The appropriate information for each is obtained from the motor nameplate.
3. Make a written diagram of the objective. A written diagram is required for the 115 V connection and 230 V connection. See Figure D15. T5 and T8 are listed separately because they are to be switched. Also, L1 and L2 are listed separately because they are power lines. No attempt has been made to simplify the objective.

115 V Connection		230 V Connection	
Forward	**Reverse**	**Forward**	**Reverse**
T5 to T1 and T3	T5 to T2 and T4	T5 to T2 and T3	T5 to T4
T8 to T2 and T4	T8 to T1 and T3	T8 to T4	T8 to T2 and T3
L1 to T1 and T3	L1 to T1 and T3	L1 to T1	L1 to T1
L2 to T2 to T4	L2 to T2 to T4	L2 to T4	L2 to T4

FIGURE D15

4. Remove common connections that are not power lines. See Figure D16. The connection L2 to T2 to T4 is removed from the 115 V connection because the connection is the same for both directions and because L2 does not have to be switched. L2 does not have to be switched because it is a neutral wire on 115 V circuits. No connections are removed from the 230 V connection because L1 and L2 are hot wires on 230 V circuits.

115 V Connection		230 V Connection	
Forward	**Reverse**	**Forward**	**Reverse**
T5 to T1 and T3	T5 to T2 and T4	T5 to T2 and T3	T5 to T4
T8 to T2 and T4	T8 to T1 and T3	T8 to T4	T8 to T2 and T3
L1 to T1 and T3	L1 to T1 and T3	L1 to T1	L1 to T1
—	—	L2 to T4	L2 to T4

FIGURE D16

5. Use one name for the remaining common connections. See Figure D17. In the simplified objective for the 115 V connection, T1 and T3 are wired together and named T1. T2 and T4 are wired together and named T2. L2 is to be connected to T2 and T4 and named T2. In the simplified objective for the 230 V connection, T2 and T3 are wired together and named T2.

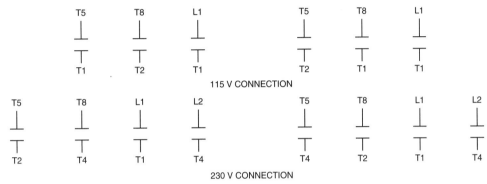

115 V Connection		230 V Connection	
Forward	**Reverse**	**Forward**	**Reverse**
T5 to T1	T5 to T2	T5 to T2	T5 to T4
T8 to T2	T8 to T1	T8 to T4	T8 to T2
L1 to T1	L1 to T1	L1 to T1	L1 to T1
—	—	L2 to T4	L2 to T4

FIGURE D17

6. Convert the written objective into a diagram that shows the placement of electrical contacts. See Figure D18.

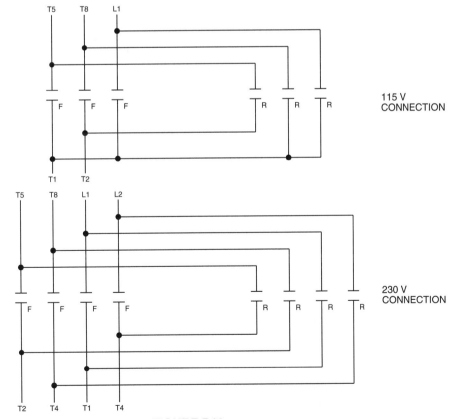

FIGURE D18

7. Draw the wiring diagram. See Figure D19.

FIGURE D19

The internal connections change within the motor as a result of the high- and low-voltage wiring. See Figure D20.

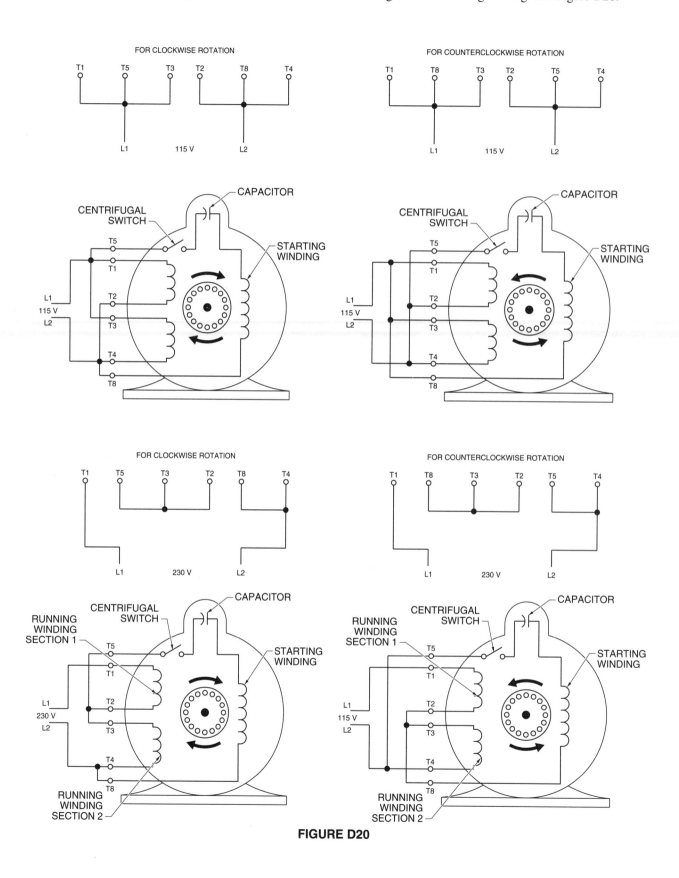

FIGURE D20

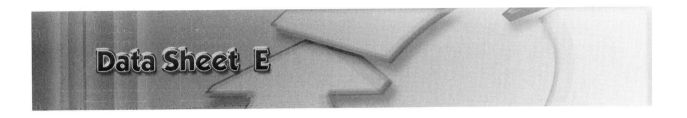

Coding Systems

A coding system may be added to the loads in timing circuits to determine the condition of a load for each sequence of the circuit operation. For example, a code of reset, timing, and timed out may be added to a circuit that uses an ON-delay timer. This coding system is useful in understanding the control circuit and can also be used to design circuits that use timers.

A common ON-delay timer used in a circuit that includes the standard sequence of reset, timing, and timed out has only eight possibilities for any output load. See Figure E1.

TIMER CODING SYSTEM			
Output	Reset	Timing	Timed Out
1	O	O	O
2	O	O	X
3	O	X	O
4	O	X	X
5	X	O	O
6	X	O	X
7	X	X	O
8	X	X	X

O = load de-energized
X = load energized

FIGURE E1

The table may be simplified by eliminating the sequences of OOO and XXX because they do not represent a useful control function. In the case of OOO, the load is de-energized all the time. In the case of XXX, the load is energized all the time. The other six possibilities provide control sequences that are useful and can be accomplished through the contacts normally provided on a timer.

Counting a Coding Table in Contact Arrangements

Timers are normally provided with NO and NC time-delay and instantaneous contacts. By using the timer contacts in various configurations, certain contact arrangements can be associated directly with the remaining six sequence codes in Figure E1.

For example, if an NO time-delay contact is connected in series with a load, the code of OOX results. See Figure E2. Any NO time-delay contact connected in series with a load provides the sequence of OOX. Thus, an electrician can develop a simple table with all six possible combinations that immediately shows which contacts to use and how to connect them for any given sequence. See Figure E3.

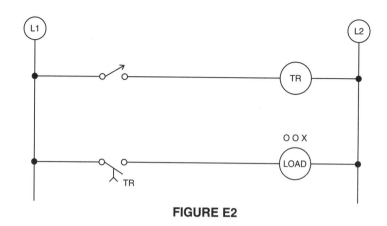

FIGURE E2

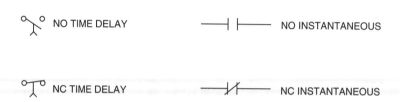

SEQUENCE CODE	CIRCUIT CONNECTION
O O X	
O X O	
O X X	
X O O	
X X O	
X O X	

FIGURE E3

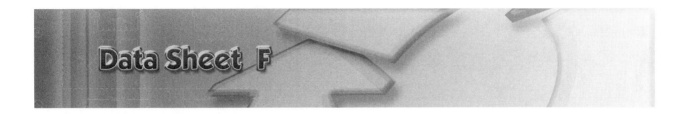

Basic Timing Circuit Design

The first step in designing a timing circuit is to list each load according to its requirements in the circuit. The second step is to list the control devices, such as pushbuttons, etc. that are needed. For example, a circuit is required to control the length of time a cake must bake in an oven and indicate by a bell when it must be removed. First, two loads must be controlled, the oven and the bell. The code for the bell is OOX because the bell signals the end of timing. The code for the oven is OXO because the oven bakes for a predetermined length of time. The first part of the circuit is designed from this information and use of a code table. See Figure F1.

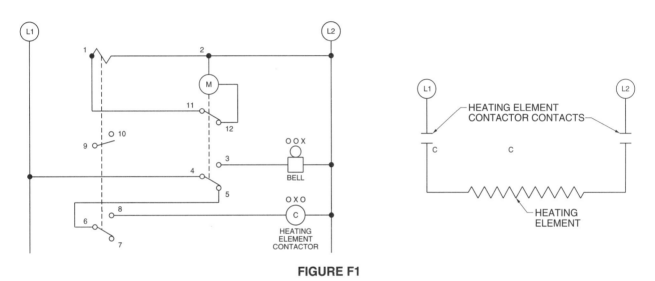

FIGURE F1

The next step in completing the timing circuit is to add the control devices necessary to control the timer and loads. Two controls are required, one to signal the start and end of the baking process and another to control the oven temperature. An ON/OFF switch may be used to signal the start and end of the process, and a temperature switch may be used to control oven temperature. Adding these two controls completes the timing circuit. See Figure F2.

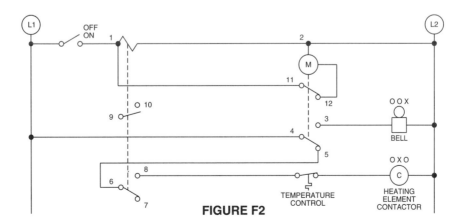

FIGURE F2

Data Sheet G

MODEL G RECYCLE TIMER

OPERATION

OFF CYCLE BEGINS TIMING WHEN SUPPLY VOLTAGE IS APPLIED. INTERNAL RELAY ENERGIZES AND ON CYCLE BEGINS TIMING ON COMPLETION OF DELAY. TIMER CONTINUES CYCLING UNTIL SUPPLY VOLTAGE IS REMOVED. ON AND OFF CYCLES MAY BE SYMMETRICAL OR ASYMMETRICAL.

MODEL G

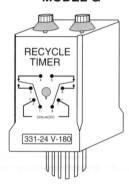

RECYCLE TIMER

COIL/AC/DC

331-24 V-180

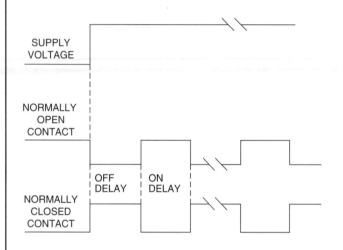

SUPPLY VOLTAGE

NORMALLY OPEN CONTACT

OFF DELAY | ON DELAY

NORMALLY CLOSED CONTACT

SPECIFICATIONS

MODEL	G
VOLTAGE	12, 24, 120, 230 VAC/DC
TIMING RANGE	.3-30 SECONDS .6-60 SECONDS 1.8-180 SECONDS 3-300 SECONDS
ACCURACY	± 6%
REPEATABILITY	± 3%
RECYCLE TIME	100 ms
CONTACTS	DPDT
CONTACT RATING	10 A @ 120 V AC RESISTIVE
OPERATING TEMPERATURE	– 20° C TO +65° C
STORAGE TEMPERATURE	– 30° C TO +80° C
HUMIDITY TOLERANCE	0%-97% W/O CONDENSATION

DIMENSIONS

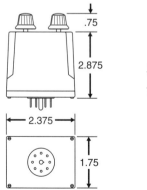

.75

2.875

2.375

1.75

WIRING

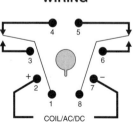

COIL/AC/DC

ORDERING INFORMATION

SPECIFY MODEL, VOLTAGE, AND TIMING RANGE.

EXAMPLE: G-24 V-100 SECONDS

Data Sheet H

MODEL A OPERATE DELAY RELAY

OPERATION

TIME DELAY BEGINS WHEN SUPPLY VOLTAGE IS APPLIED TO COIL. INTERNAL RELAY ENERGIZES ON COMPLETION OF DELAY PERIOD AND REMAINS ENERGIZED UNTIL SUPPLY VOLTAGE IS REMOVED.

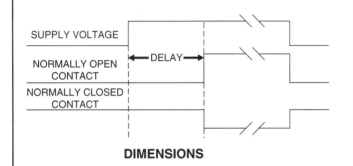

SUPPLY VOLTAGE

NORMALLY OPEN CONTACT — DELAY

NORMALLY CLOSED CONTACT

SPECIFICATIONS

MODEL	A
VOLTAGE	12, 24, 120, 230 VAC/DC
TIMING RANGE	1-10 SECONDS 1-60 SECONDS 1-100 SECONDS 1-300 SECONDS
ACCURACY	± 6%
REPEATABILITY	± 3%
RECYCLE TIME	100 ms
CONTACTS	DPDT
CONTACT RATING	10 A @ 120 V AC RESISTIVE
OPERATING TEMPERATURE	– 20° C TO +65° C
STORAGE TEMPERATURE	– 30° C TO +80° C
HUMIDITY TOLERANCE	0%-97% W/O CONDENSATION

DIMENSIONS

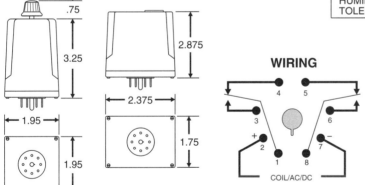

.75

3.25

2.875

1.95

2.375

1.75

1.95

WIRING

COIL/AC/DC

ORDERING INFORMATION

SPECIFY MODEL, VOLTAGE, AND TIMING RANGE.

EXAMPLE: A-24 V-100 SECONDS

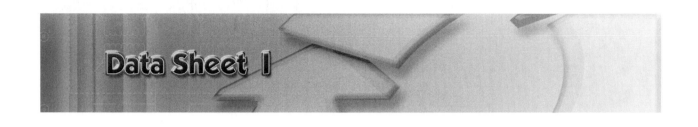

Data Sheet I

MODEL C RELEASE DELAY RELAY

OPERATION

SUPPLY VOLTAGE IS CONSTANTLY APPLIED TO COIL. INTERNAL RELAYS ENERGIZE WHEN CONTROL SWITCH IS CLOSED. TIMING BEGINS WHEN CONTROL SWITCH IS OPENED. DELAY IS RESET BY RECLOSING CONTROL SWITCH. RELAY DE-ENERGIZES ON COMPLETION OF DELAY PERIOD.

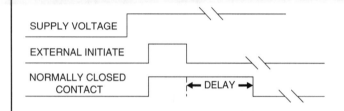

WIRING

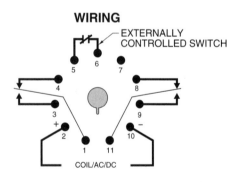

SPECIFICATIONS

MODEL	C
VOLTAGE	24, 120 VAC/DC
TIMING RANGE	1-10 SECONDS 1-60 SECONDS 1-100 SECONDS 1-300 SECONDS
ACCURACY	± 6%
REPEATABILITY	_ 2.5%
RECYCLE TIME	100 ms
CONTACTS	DPDT
CONTACT RATING	10 A @ 120 V AC RESISTIVE
OPERATING TEMPERATURE	– 25° C TO +65° C
STORAGE TEMPERATURE	– 30° C TO +90° C
HUMIDITY TOLERANCE	0%-97% W/O CONDENSATION

ORDERING INFORMATION

SPECIFY MODEL, VOLTAGE, AND TIMING RANGE.

EXAMPLE: C-24 V-10 SECONDS

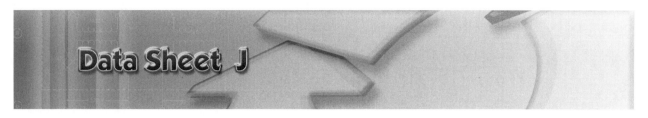

Photosensor Relay

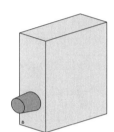

MODEL J

- Relay for photosensors with modulated infrared light
- Built-in power supply for transmitter/receiver
- For separate transmitters and receivers with max. ranges 1 m—100 m
- For combined transmitters and receivers with max. ranges 1 m—10 m
- Transmitter and receiver connections are short-circuit safe
- 10 A SPDT output relay
- LED-indication for relay ON
- AC or DC supply voltage

SPECIFICATIONS

Response frequency
Max. 10 pulses/sec

Duration of light/darkness
Both: Min. 50 ms

Connections for transmitters
Voltage/current = 3.5 VDC / 100 mA

Idle voltage = 5 VDC

Short-circuit current = 500 mA

Connection: Pins 6 and 7
    Pin 7 positive
    Short-circuit safe

Connections for receivers
Voltage = 12 VDC

Current: Light: 15 mA
    Dark: 1 mA – 4 mA

Idle voltage = 12 VDC

Short-circuit current = 75 mA

Connection: Pins 5 and 6
    Pin 5 positive
    Short-circuit safe

WIRING DIAGRAMS

Note: Standard supply voltage is 115 VAC on pin 2 and 10.

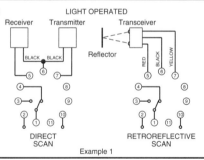

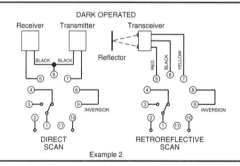

MODE OF OPERATION

Relay is used in conjunction with separate infrared transmitters and receivers and retroreflective heads.
Photosensors work with infrared, modulated light and because of modulation, are insensitive to environmental light.
Transmitter is a Ga-As diode and receiver is a phototransistor.
When sensing by reflection either a reflector or other materials can be used, such as plastics, textiles, metal, paper, glass, etc.

Example 1 (LIGHT OPERATED)
Relay releases when light beam is interrupted. Relay also releases in case one or more cable(s) between photosensors and relay are disconnected and in case of power failure.

Example 2 (DARK OPERATED)
Relay operates when light beam is interrupted. Relay also operates in case one or more cable(s) between photosensors and relay are disconnected.

OPERATIONAL DIAGRAM

Supply voltage
Light beam interrupted
Ex 1 Relay ON (light operated)
Ex 2 Relay ON (dark operated)

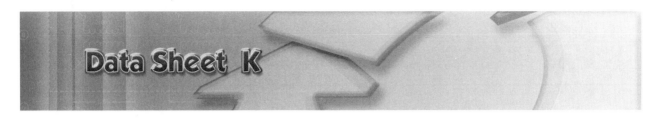

Inductive/Capacitive Sensor Relay

MODEL K

- Relay for inductive and capacitive sensors without amplifier
- Voltage and current limitation in sensor circuit (8 VDC, 8 mA)
- Relay locks in OFF position by cable failures
- 5 A DPDT output relay
- LED-indication for relay ON
- AC or DC supply voltage

SPECIFICATIONS

Sensor voltage
Pins 5 and 6 or 6 and 7:
8 VDC
Pin 6 positive

Sensor current
Activated: < 1 mA
Not activated: > 3 mA

Short-circuit current
Max. 8 mA

Connection cable
Unshielded PVC core. Can be extended if required, maximum resistance = 100Ω .

Sensing range
0.5 mm – 40 mm depending on sensor

Sensing speed
Max. 10 operations/sec

Pulse time
Min. 20 ms

Subject of detection
Solid, fluid, or granulated substances

WIRING DIAGRAM

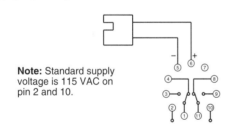

Note: Standard supply voltage is 115 VAC on pin 2 and 10.

MODE OF OPERATION

Relay operates by activation of sensor.
It releases automatically in case of cable failure.

OPERATIONAL DIAGRAM

| Supply voltage |
| Sensor activated |
| Cable failure |
| Relay ON |

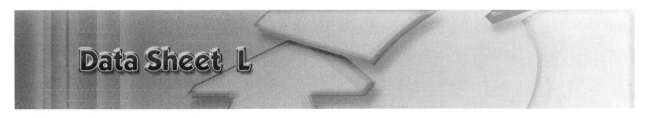

Multiple Inductive/Capacitive Sensor Relay

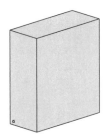

MODEL L

- **Bistable relay for 2 inductive or capacitive sensors without amplifier**
- **Voltage and current limitation in sensor circuits (8 VDC, 8 mA)**
- **5 A SPDT output relay**
- **AC or DC supply voltage**

SPECIFICATIONS

Sensor voltage
Pins 5 and 6 or 6 and 7:
8 VDC
Pin 6 positive

Sensor current
Activated: < 1 mA
Not activated: > 3 mA

Short-circuit current
Max. 8 mA

Connection cable
Unshielded PVC core. Can be extended if required, maximum resistance = 100Ω .

Sensing range
0.5 mm – 40 mm, depending on the sensor

Sensing speed
Max. 10 operations/sec

Pulse time
Min. 20 ms

Subject of detection
Solid, fluid, or granulated substances.

WIRING DIAGRAM

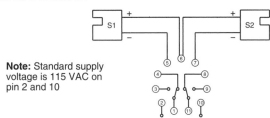

Note: Standard supply voltage is 115 VAC on pin 2 and 10

MODE OF OPERATION

Being a bistable relay, it is used with two proximity sensors.

Relay operates when one sensor (S1) is activated momentarily and then remains operated.

Relay releases when other sensor (S2) is activated momentarily or when supply voltage is interrupted.

If both sensors are activated simultaneously, relay releases or shall not operate respectively. Sensor (S2) has priority.

OPERATIONAL DIAGRAM

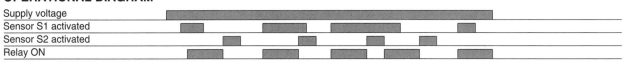

Supply voltage
Sensor S1 activated
Sensor S2 activated
Relay ON

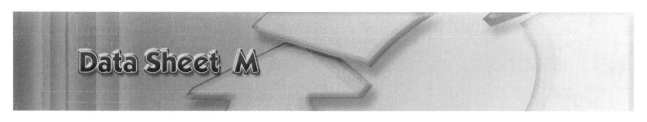

Data Sheet M

Load Guard Relay

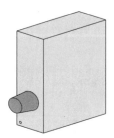

MODEL M

- Load guard for asynchronous motors and other symmetrical loads
- Measures phase difference between motor current and voltage
- Measuring range: Cos φ = 0– 0.9 with current metering transformer
- Knob – adjustable
- Delayed function on start
- 10 A SPDT output relay
- LED-indication for relay ON
- AC or DC supply voltage

SPECIFICATIONS

Supply voltage
3 x 220 VAC
Other voltages upon request.

Measuring range
Cos φ = 0 - 0.9
With current measuring transformer.

Hysteresis
10° equaling approx 1 graduation mark.

Adjustment
Knob-adjustable with absolute scale.

Measuring of current phase
Measuring input for connection of current metering transformer:
Pins 8 and 11
Voltage from current metering transformer: 0.1 V_{peak} - 4 V_{peak}. If current is below 2.5 A conductor may be drawn through central hole of transformer many times, so that number of turns multiplied by current consumption is inside current range of transformer. Transformer should be mounted so current flows from front towards rear of transformer.

Measuring
Voltage as well as current are measured on phase connected to pin 5.

Inversion
Output signal can be inverted by interconnecting pins 9 and 11.

Reaction time
During operation typically 0.5 sec.

WIRING DIAGRAMS

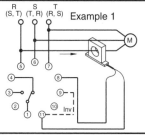

MODE OF OPERATION

System can be used for monitoring actual load of asynchronous motors. Measures angle between motor current and motor voltage, i.e. phase angle difference. This angle always exists and its change is almost proportional to actual motor load (contrary to motor current solely).
Characteristics of load depend on type of motor and phase difference. Cos φ depends upon actual load. It is recommended to adjust cos φ after practical tests.
Relay contact should be employed as a stop function in a system with external restart.

Example 1
Relay is connected to a current metering transformer as well as to a 3 φ asynchronous motor. Relay operates when cos φ is below set value. At inversion (stippled line) relay operates when cos φ exceeds set value.

Example 2
By a combination of normal and inverted functions, relay monitors whether cos φ is within a set maximum and minimum level respectively.

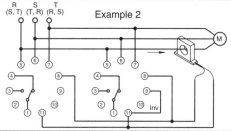

Phase Difference/Load

OPERATIONAL DIAGRAM

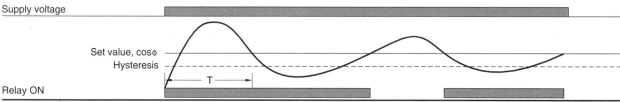

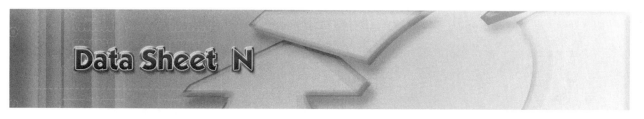

Phase Angle Error Relay

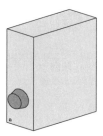

MODEL N

- • Relay for phase angle errors and phase breaking
- • Metering range for phase angle error: 5°– 15°
- • Knob-adjustable phase angle sensitivity
- • Operates irrespective of phase sequence
- • 10 A SPDT output relay
- • LED-indication for relay ON
- • Supply voltage is 3-phased metering voltage

SPECIFICATIONS

Inputs
Pins 5, 6, and 7

Metering/Supply voltage
3 x 220 VAC ⎱ ± 10 %
3 x 380 VAC ⎰

Frequency
50 Hz or 60 Hz

Reaction time on phase angle error
1 sec is available upon request with
reaction times up to approx. 4 sec.

Phase angle sensitivity
5° - 15° ±10%

Amplitude sensitivity
± 30%

Hysteresis
Approx. 2°

WIRING DIAGRAM

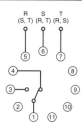

MODE OF OPERATION

Relay meters on its own 3φ supply
voltage and controls mutual phase angle.
It operates irrespective of phase sequence
when angle error is less than set value.

In case of interruption of a phase, relay
releases provided that mutual phase angle
error between flawless phases and phase
possibly regenerated by electric motors
connected exceeds set value.

Even if phase angle error does not exceed
set value, relay shall release in case of
phase breaking provided that voltage
regenerated is below 70% of nominal voltage.

OPERATIONAL DIAGRAM

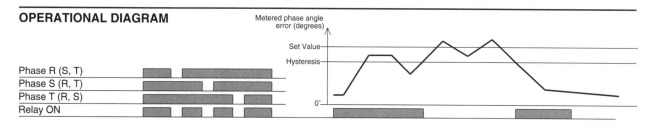

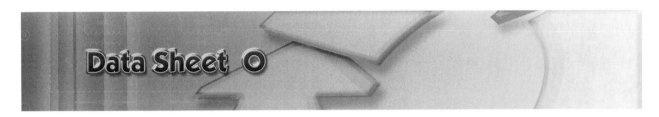

Data Sheet O

Phase Sequence Relay

MODEL O

- **Phase sequence/Phase breaking relay**
- **Measures ON voltage**
- **10 A SPDT output relay**
- **LED indication for relay ON**
- **Supply voltage is 3φ measuring voltage**

SPECIFICATIONS

Inputs
Pins 5, 6, and 7

Measuring voltage – Supply voltage
3 x 220 VAC ⎫ ± 10%
3 x 380 VAC ⎭

Measuring voltage also works as supply voltage.

Frequency
45 Hz – 65 Hz

WIRING DIAGRAMS

R = L1
S = L2
T = L3

Example 1

Example 2

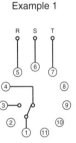
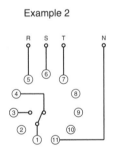

MODE OF OPERATION

Relay measures on its own 3φ supply voltage and operates when all phases are present and phase sequence is correct.

Example 1
Relay releases in case of interruption of one phase, provided that voltage regenerated by electric motors of interrupted phase does not exceed 50% of nominal voltage.

Example 2
If value of regenerated voltage is somewhat higher than 50% of nominal voltage, system can be brought to release when zero line of supply voltage is connected to pin 11, as sensitivity of system is thereby improved.

At regenerated voltages, amplitude depends on size and load of connected electric motor.

In practice, value of regenerated voltage can be near the same as value of supply voltage.

OPERATIONAL DIAGRAM

Phase R Pin 5			S	T	R	
Phase S Pin 6			R	S	S	
Phase T Pin 7			T	R	T	
Relay ON						

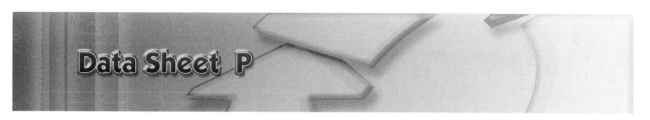

Current Metering Relay

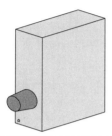

MODEL P

- Current metering relay for AC
- Metering range: 0.1 A– 500 A (peak) with current metering transformer
- Knob-adjustable trip point
- Latching at set level possible
- 10 A SPDT output relay
- LED-indication for relay ON
- AC or DC supply voltage

SPECIFICATIONS

Input voltage
Pins 5 and 7: 0.1 V– 4 V
Max. 50 V
Pin 5 positive

Latching
Relay shall latch at set level when pins 8 and 9 are interconnected.

Hysteresis
Approx. 10%
Hysteresis can be extended to approx 75% by connecting a resistor between pins 8 and 9. Resistor limits are 1 MΩ and 15 kΩ. Hysteresis increases by decreasing resistance.

AC Measurements 1φ or 3φ
Made in conjunction with one current metering transformer. These transformers deliver an output voltage between 0.1 V and 4 V being proportional with current flowing in a conductor, drawn through center hole of transformer.

WIRING DIAGRAMS

CONNECT PINS 2 AND 10 TO POWER LINES L1 AND L2

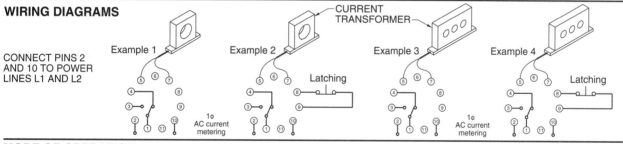

MODE OF OPERATION

Example 1
AC CURRENT METERING (1φ)
Relay operates when current reaches set value. Relay releases when current drops at least 10% below set value (see hysteresis) or by connecting supply voltage.

Example 2
AC CURRENT METERING (1φ) LATCHING
Relay operates when current reaches set value and then latches in operating position.

Relay releases by removing latch, i.e. by opening contact between pins 8 and 9, provided that current has dropped at least 10% below set value (see hysteresis), or by disconnecting supply voltage.

Example 3
AC CURRENT METERING (3φ)
Relay operates when current in any phase reaches set value. Relay releases when current in all 3 phases has dropped at least 10% below set value (see hysteresis) or by

disconnecting supply voltage.

Example 4
AC CURRENT METERING (3φ) LATCHING
Relay operates when current in any phase reaches set value and then latches in operating position. Relay releases by removing latch, i.e. by opening contact between pins 8 and 9, provided that current in all 3 phases has dropped at least 10% below set value (see hysteresis), or by disconnecting supply voltage.

OPERATIONAL DIAGRAMS

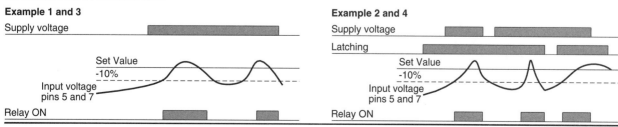

\	\	\	ENCLOSURE TYPES	\
Type	**Use**	**Service Conditions**	**Tests**	**Comments**
1	Indoor	No unusual	Rod entry, rust resistance	
3	Outdoor	Windblown dust, rain, sleet, and ice on enclosure	Rain, external icing, dust, and rust resistance	Do not provide protection against internal condensation or internal icing
3R	Outdoor	Falling rain and ice on enclosure	Rod entry, rain, external icing, and rust resistance	Do not provide protection against dust, internal condensation, or internal icing
4	Indoor/outdoor	Windblown dust and rain, splashing water, hose-directed water, and ice on enclosure	Hosedown, external icing, and rust resistance	Do not provide protection against internal condensation or internal icing
4X	Indoor/outdoor	Corrosion, windblown dust and rain, splashing water, hose-directed water, and ice on enclosure	Hosedown, external icing, and corrosion resistance	Do not provide protection against internal condensation or internal icing
6	Indoor/outdoor	Occasional temporary submersion at a limited depth		
6P	Indoor/outdoor	Prolonged submersion at a limited depth		
7	Indoor locations classified as Class I, Groups A, B, C, or D, as defined in the NEC®	Withstand and contain an internal explosion of specified gases, contain an explosion sufficiently so an explosive gas-air mixture in the atmosphere is not ignited	Explosion, hydrostatic, and temperature	Enclosed heat-generating devices shall not cause external surfaces to reach temperatures capable of igniting explosive gas-air mixtures in the atmosphere.
9	Indoor locations classified as Class II, Groups E or G, as defined in the NEC®	Dust	Dust penetration, temperature, and gasket aging	Enclosed heat-generating devices shall not cause external surfaces to reach temperatures capable of igniting explosive gas-air mixtures in the atmosphere
12	Indoor	Dust, falling dirt, and dripping noncorrosive liquids	Drip, dust, and rust resistance	Do not provide protection against internal condensation
13	Indoor	Dust, spraying water, oil, and noncorrosive coolant	Oil explosion and rust resistance	Do not provide protection against internal condensation

INDUSTRIAL ELECTRICAL SYMBOLS . . .

DISCONNECT	CIRCUIT INTERRUPTER	CIRCUIT BREAKER WITH THERMAL OL	CIRCUIT BREAKER WITH MAGNETIC OL	CIRCUIT BREAKER W/ THERMAL AND MAGNETIC OL

LIMIT SWITCHES

NORMALLY OPEN	NORMALLY CLOSED	FOOT SWITCHES	PRESSURE AND VACUUM SWITCHES	LIQUID LEVEL SWITCH	TEMPERATURE-ACTUATED SWITCH	FLOW SWITCH (AIR, WATER, ETC.)
		NO	NO	NO	NO	NO
HELD CLOSED	HELD OPEN	NC	NC	NC	NC	NC

SPEED (PLUGGING)		ANTI-PLUG	SYMBOLS FOR STATIC SWITCHING CONTROL DEVICES
F ... R	F ... R	F ... R	STATIC SWITCHING CONTROL IS A METHOD OF SWITCHING ELECTRICAL CIRCUITS WITHOUT USE OF CONTACTS, PRIMARILY BY SOLID-STATE DEVICES. USE SYMBOLS SHOWN IN TABLE AND ENCLOSE THEM IN A DIAMOND.

INPUT COIL   OUTPUT NO   LIMIT SWITCH NO   LIMIT SWITCH NC

SELECTOR

TWO-POSITION	THREE-POSITION	TWO-POSITION SELECTOR PUSHBUTTON

TWO-POSITION

J K

○ ─ ○ A1

○   ○ A2

	J	K
A1	X	
A2		X

X-CONTACT CLOSED

THREE-POSITION

K
J ↑ L
○   ○ A1

○   ○ A2

	J	K	L
A1	X		
A2			X

X-CONTACT CLOSED

TWO-POSITION SELECTOR PUSHBUTTON

A   B
1 ○   ○ 2

3 ○   ○ 4

CONTACTS	SELECTOR POSITION			
	A		B	
	BUTTON		BUTTON	
	FREE	DEPRESSED	FREE	DEPRESSED
1-2	X			
3-4		X	X	X

X - CONTACT CLOSED

PUSHBUTTONS

MOMENTARY CONTACT				MAINTAINED CONTACT		ILLUMINATED
SINGLE CIRCUIT	DOUBLE CIRCUIT	MUSHROOM HEAD	WOBBLE STICK	TWO SINGLE CIRCUIT	ONE DOUBLE CIRCUIT	
NO	NO AND NC					
NC						

. . . INDUSTRIAL ELECTRICAL SYMBOLS . . .

CONTACTS

INSTANT OPERATING				TIMED CONTACTS - CONTACT ACTION RETARDED AFTER COIL IS:			
WITH BLOWOUT		WITHOUT BLOWOUT		ENERGIZED		DE-ENERGIZED	
NO	NC	NO	NC	NOTC	NCTO	NOTO	NCTC

OVERLOAD RELAYS

THERMAL	MAGNETIC

SUPPLEMENTARY CONTACT SYMBOLS

SPST NO		SPST NC		SPDT		TERMS
SINGLE BREAK	DOUBLE BREAK	SINGLE BREAK	DOUBLE BREAK	SINGLE BREAK	DOUBLE BREAK	SPST SINGLE-POLE, SINGLE-THROW
						SPDT SINGLE-POLE, DOUBLE-THROW
DPST, 2NO		DPST, 2NC		DPDT		DPST DOUBLE-POLE, SINGLE-THROW
SINGLE BREAK	DOUBLE BREAK	SINGLE BREAK	DOUBLE BREAK	SINGLE BREAK	DOUBLE BREAK	DPDT DOUBLE-POLE, DOUBLE-THROW
						NO NORMALLY OPEN
						NC NORMALLY CLOSED

METER (INSTRUMENT)

INDICATE TYPE BY LETTER	TO INDICATE FUNCTION OF METER OR INSTRUMENT, PLACE SPECIFIED LETTER OR LETTERS WITHIN SYMBOL.			
	AM or A	AMMETER	VA	VOLTMETER
	AH	AMPERE HOUR	VAR	VARMETER
	µA	MICROAMMETER	VARH	VARHOUR METER
	mA	MILLAMMETER	W	WATTMETER
	PF	POWER FACTOR	WH	WATTHOUR METER
	V	VOLTMETER		

PILOT LIGHTS

INDICATE COLOR BY LETTER	
NON PUSH-TO-TEST	PUSH-TO-TEST

INDUCTORS

IRON CORE
AIR CORE

COILS

		DUAL-VOLTAGE MAGNET COILS		BLOWOUT COIL
		HIGH-VOLTAGE	LOW-VOLTAGE	
		LINK	LINKS	
		1 2 3 4	1 2 3 4	

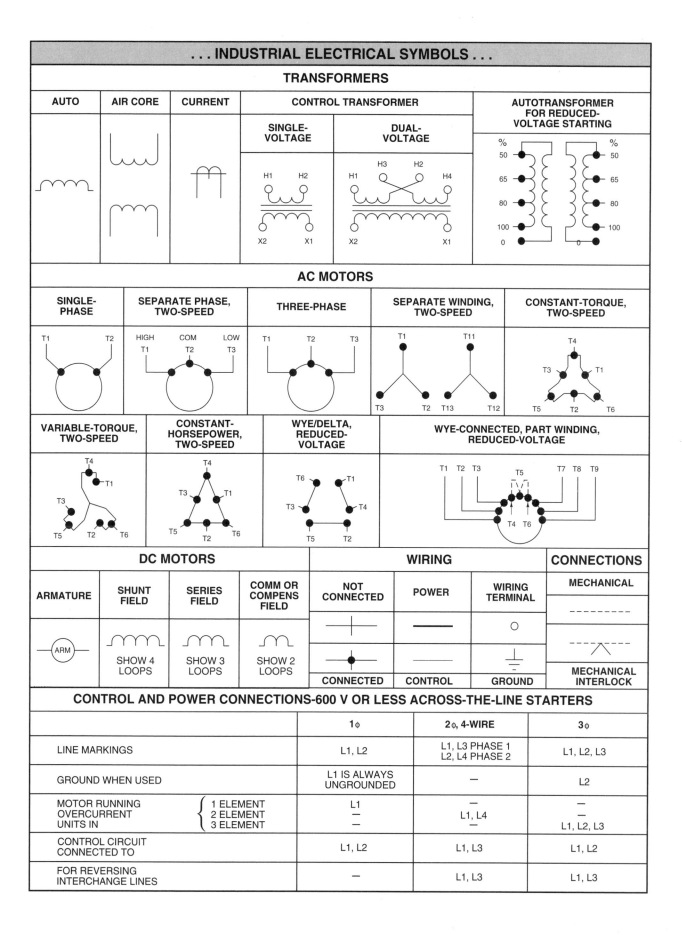

. . . INDUSTRIAL ELECTRICAL SYMBOLS . . .

TRANSFORMERS

AUTO	AIR CORE	CURRENT	CONTROL TRANSFORMER		AUTOTRANSFORMER FOR REDUCED-VOLTAGE STARTING
			SINGLE-VOLTAGE	DUAL-VOLTAGE	

AC MOTORS

SINGLE-PHASE	SEPARATE PHASE, TWO-SPEED	THREE-PHASE	SEPARATE WINDING, TWO-SPEED	CONSTANT-TORQUE, TWO-SPEED

VARIABLE-TORQUE, TWO-SPEED	CONSTANT-HORSEPOWER, TWO-SPEED	WYE/DELTA, REDUCED-VOLTAGE	WYE-CONNECTED, PART WINDING, REDUCED-VOLTAGE

DC MOTORS / WIRING / CONNECTIONS

ARMATURE	SHUNT FIELD	SERIES FIELD	COMM OR COMPENS FIELD	NOT CONNECTED	POWER	WIRING TERMINAL	MECHANICAL
	SHOW 4 LOOPS	SHOW 3 LOOPS	SHOW 2 LOOPS	CONNECTED	CONTROL	GROUND	MECHANICAL INTERLOCK

CONTROL AND POWER CONNECTIONS-600 V OR LESS ACROSS-THE-LINE STARTERS

	1φ	2φ, 4-WIRE	3φ
LINE MARKINGS	L1, L2	L1, L3 PHASE 1 / L2, L4 PHASE 2	L1, L2, L3
GROUND WHEN USED	L1 IS ALWAYS UNGROUNDED	—	L2
MOTOR RUNNING OVERCURRENT UNITS IN — 1 ELEMENT / 2 ELEMENT / 3 ELEMENT	L1 / — / —	— / L1, L4 / —	— / — / L1, L2, L3
CONTROL CIRCUIT CONNECTED TO	L1, L2	L1, L3	L1, L2
FOR REVERSING INTERCHANGE LINES	—	L1, L3	L1, L3

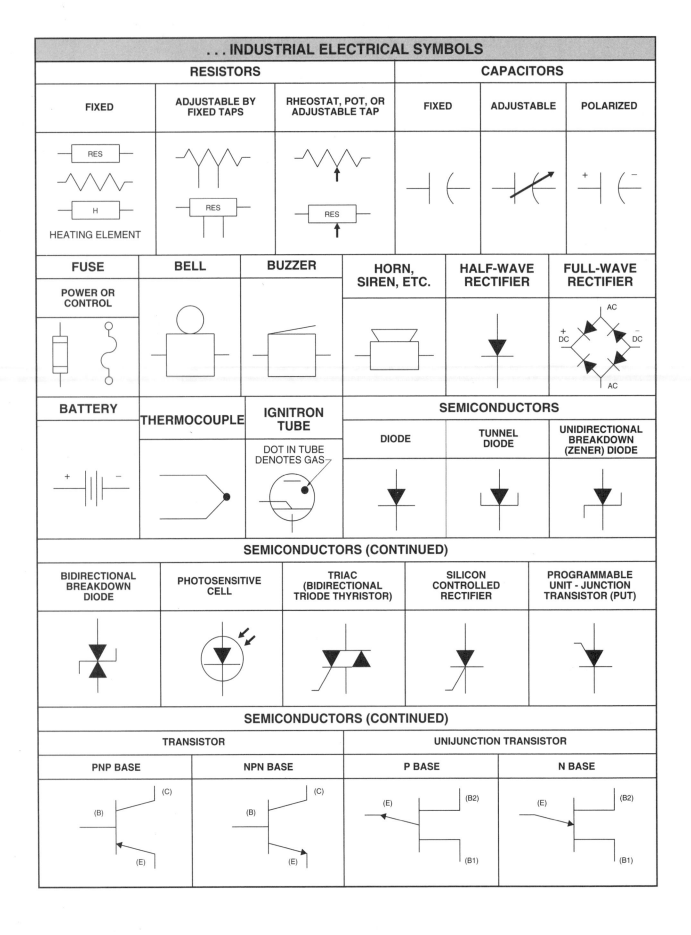